ROBERT E. KRIEGER
PUBLISHING COMPANY INC.

HUNTINGTON,
NEW YORK 11743

# Functions, Limits, and Continuity

# Functions, Limits, and Continuity

**Paulo Ribenboim**

Queen's University
Kingston, Ontario, Canada

**John Wiley & Sons, Inc.**
New York • London • Sydney

# Preface

The purpose of this book is to provide a well-grounded basis for the study of mathematical analysis. It is especially aimed at students of mathematics and physics (even gifted senior high-school students) who feel the need of understanding rather than calculating.

No previous specific knowledge of mathematics is required—only, at most, a familiarity with it as it is taught in high school.

The subject is developed from an almost common-sense beginning. My objective is to motivate and explain thoroughly all of the new ideas introduced, relating them with our everyday intuition.

I have restricted myself to a very small domain; by no means have I attempted to condense a course of Analysis into this volume.

My purpose is twofold: first, to reduce the task of studying these basic ideas to such an extent as to make it attractive; and, second, by eliminating most of the applications usually taught in calculus courses (which can be found elsewhere), to deliberately focus attention upon the first essential principles of Analysis.

An understanding of these concepts offers the first real challenge to the student of mathematics, and it is my conviction—based on teaching experience—that no serious study can be pursued until the student has mastered these notions.

This book is based on the notes of my lectures at the University of Illinois. Their general acceptance by the students induced me to publish them. I hope that the simplicity of this presentation suggests that, after all, any fundamental mathematical concept may be ultimately explained, if one desires, through some rather intuitive idea.

*Kingston, Ontario, Canada*, 1964                    PAULO RIBENBOIM

# Contents

# Sets, Correspondences

Two of the most fundamental notions in mathematics are those of SET and CORRESPONDENCE. They appear directly or indirectly in all mathematical definitions and, therefore, should be considered as *primitive notions*, which remain undefined.

The following examples illustrate cases in which we shall apply the terms set and correspondence.

We shall use the words set, COLLECTION, AGGREGATE, and CLASS of objects as synonyms.

EXAMPLES

1. The set of straight lines in the plane, passing through a given point.
2. The set of even integers.
3. The set of triangles inscribed in a given circle.
4. The set of second-degree equations with integral coefficients.

The objects or ELEMENTS in the above examples are of mathematical nature. We may also consider sets of objects of other kinds, such as the set of books on a bookshelf, or the set of students in a classroom. But we shall not deal here with this type of sets.

To indicate that an element $x$ belongs to a given set $X$, we use the notation $x \in X$. The fact that $x$ does not belong to the set $X$ is written as $x \notin X$.

Let $X$, $Y$ be two sets. We say that *a correspondence from $X$ into $Y$ is given* when we have a rule that associates to every element $x$ of $X$ an element $y$ of $Y$; $y$ is called the IMAGE of $x$ under the correspondence.

Note that we are not *defining* the notion of correspondence, but are only translating into more familiar words the term "correspondence."

EXAMPLE. Let $X$ be the set $\{1, 2, 3, 4, 5, \ldots\}$ of natural numbers and $Y$ the set $\{2, 4, 6, 8, 10, \ldots\}$ of even natural numbers. The rule that to each number associates its double (for example, $1 \rightarrow 2, 2 \rightarrow 4, \ldots, n \rightarrow 2n,$ $\ldots$) establishes a correspondence from $X$ into $Y$. In this example, we call attention to two facts: (*1*) every element of $Y$ is the image of some element in $X$, and (*2*) any two *distinct* elements in $X$ have *distinct* images.

This suggests the following terminology.

A correspondence from $X$ ONTO $Y$ is a correspondence from $X$ into $Y$ such that *every* element of $Y$ is the image of some element of $X$.

Thus, the correspondence in the above example is onto $Y$.

A correspondence from $X$ into $Y$ is said to be ONE-TO-ONE when any two distinct points in $X$ have distinct images in $Y$.

Thus, the correspondence in the preceding example is one-to-one.

EXAMPLE OF A CORRESPONDENCE FROM $X$ ONTO $Y$, WHICH IS NOT ONE-TO-ONE. Let $X$ be the set of circles in the plane, having integral radii, and let $Y$ be the set of natural numbers $\{1, 2, 3, \ldots\}$. The correspondence, which associates to each such circle its radius, is onto the set $Y$, but is not one-to-one, since two different circles may have the same radius when they have different centers.

EXAMPLE OF A CORRESPONDENCE FROM $X$ INTO $Y$, WHICH IS ONE-TO-ONE BUT NOT ONTO $Y$. Let $X$ and $Y$ be both equal to the set of natural numbers; the correspondence, which associates to every natural number its square, is one-to-one, but not onto $Y$.

We shall deal later with certain types of correspondences, which will be called FUNCTIONS.

In the case of a correspondence from the set of natural numbers into a set $X$, we shall use a special name: SEQUENCE of elements of $X$. The images of $1, 2, \ldots, n, \ldots$ will be denoted respectively by $x_1, x_2, \ldots, x_n, \ldots$, and will be called the TERMS of the sequence. The sequence itself will be denoted by $(x_1, x_2, \ldots, x_n, \ldots)$ or also $(x_n)$.

This completes for the moment our brief comment about sets and related fundamental notions. Primarily, it has amounted to language expressions. We deliberately have avoided the development of an analysis that approximates a theory of sets, since it is contrary to the spirit of this book to introduce notions that are not well motivated and essential to the exposition. Moreover, we do not wish to give the false impression that formally developed set theory is necessary to an exposition at this level of those fundamental concepts of analysis that are found here.

Any other set-theoretical notions, which may be needed later, will be treated in subsequent chapters.

# 2

# Integers and Fractions

Since most of us know the integers, . . ., $-3$, $-2$, $-1$, 0, 1, 2, 3, . . ., their use and operations, we shall not discuss here the necessary steps in order to define the integers out from purely logical notions.

We recall, however, that a notion of *inequality of integers* is defined as follows.

If $a$, $b$ are integers, $a$ is *less than or equal to b* when the difference $b - a$ is either 0 or a natural number; then, $b$ *is greater than or equal to a*, and we write $a \leqslant b$ or $b \geqslant a$ to express this fact. Note that $a \leqslant a$ (for every integer $a$).

When $a$, $b$ are distinct integers and $a \leqslant b$, we say that $a$ is *strictly smaller than b* or, equivalently, $b$ is *strictly greater than a*, and we write $a < b$, or $b > a$. Note that it is false that $a < a$, for any integer $a$.

The integers $a$ such that $a \geqslant 0$ are called *positive integers;* in particular, 0 is a positive integer.

The integers $a$ such that $a > 0$, that is, the natural numbers, are said to be *strictly positive* integers.

We use similar definitions for negative integers (those $a$ such that $a \leqslant 0$) and strictly negative integers (those $a$ such that $a < 0$).

Thus, 0 is the only integer that is both positive and negative.*

With this notion of inequality, the set of integers becomes a LINEARLY ORDERED SET; this means that the following properties are true, as we may verify at once.

---

* The consideration of 0 as a *positive integer* is purely a matter of convention which, we recognize, is not followed by most authors. However, this practice is of some advantage in stating facts about mathematical systems that have a "notion of inequality" and a "zero element."

*Reflexive property.* $a \leqslant a$ for every integer $a$.
*Antisymmetric property.* If $a$, $b$ are integers, $a \leqslant b$ and $b \leqslant a$, then $a = b$.
*Transitive property.* If $a$, $b$, $c$ are integers, if $a \leqslant b$, $b \leqslant c$, then $a \leqslant c$.
*Linear property.* If $a$, $b$ are any integers, then either $a \leqslant b$ or $b \leqslant a$.

Moreover, the following *compatibility properties* linking the operations of addition and multiplication with the notion of inequality are also true.

If $a$, $b$, $c$ are integers and $b < c$, then $a + b < a + c$.
If $a$, $b$, $c$ are integers, $a > 0$, $b < c$, then $ab < ac$.

Finally, we point out that the set of natural numbers is WELL ORDERED; this means:

*Every collection of natural numbers contains a smallest integer* (provided it contains at least one number). *

We recall that this property is proved by using the PRINCIPLE OF FINITE INDUCTION, one of the essential properties of the natural numbers.

*If a set S of natural numbers contains the number 1 and contains the number $n + 1$ every time it contains a number n, then S is equal to the set of all the natural numbers.*

There follows the proof that the set of natural numbers is well-ordered.

Let $M$ be a set of natural numbers without a smallest element. We shall prove that $M$ has no elements, that is, $M$ is the empty set.

The number 1 is not in $M$, otherwise it would be its smallest element.

We may consider the set $S$ of all natural numbers $n$, which are strictly smaller than every element of $M$. Clearly, if $m \in M$, then $m \notin S$, since $m < m$ is false.

The number 1 is in $S$.

Next, we prove that if a natural number $n$ belongs to $S$, then $n + 1$ belongs also to $S$. By hypothesis, $n < m$ for every integer $m$ belonging to the set $M$. If $n + 1$ is not in $S$, it means that some element $m$ of $M$ is not strictly greater than $n + 1$; that is, $n + 1 < m$ is false. Since $n < m$, it follows that $m = n + 1$ is the smallest element of $M$, contrary to our hypothesis. Thus, $n + 1$ belongs indeed to the set $S$.

Therefore, the set $S$ has the properties indicated in the principle of finite induction: it contains 1 and, with every natural number $n$ in $S$, it contains $n + 1$. Thus, $S$ must be equal to the set of all natural numbers. Consequently, $M$ cannot contain any natural number $m$, since $m \in M$ implies $m \notin S$, which is false. Therefore, $M$ is the empty set.

Now, turning our attention to the fractions or rational numbers, let us recall briefly their definition and main properties.

---

* The set without elements, called the EMPTY SET, also may be considered and, in the theory of sets, plays a role similar to the number 0 among the integers.

It is well known that if $a$, $b$ are integers and $b \neq 0$, in general there is no integer $q$ (quotient) such that $bq = a$; for example, there is no integer $q$ for which $2q = 1$. We may express this fact by saying that the division of integers cannot generally be performed in such a way that the quotient be an integer.

Thus, if we wish to perform division of integers, without restriction (except that the divisor be distinct from 0), we must *enlarge the notion of number*, creating new numbers, such as to be quotients of division of integers. These will be called fractions or rational numbers.

Each rational number $q$ will be associated to a pair of integers $(a, b)$ in a certain order ($a$ being a dividend, $b \neq 0$ a divisor), so that when a multiplication among rational numbers will be defined, then $bq = a$ must be true. From this it will follow also that $(2b)q = 2a$, $(3b)q = 3a$, and so on. Therefore, the fraction $q$ is also going to be associated to the ordered pair of integers $(2a, 2b)$, or also to $(3a, 3b)$, and so on.

These considerations suggest that a rational number will be given by an ordered pair of integers (with the second term different from 0), allowing for the fact that different ordered pairs $(a, b)$, $(a', b')$ give the same rational number provided $(a', b')$ be "proportional" to $(a, b)$.

Now we are able to understand the following concepts.

The ordered pairs of integers $(a, b)$, $(a', b')$ are said to be *equivalent* (or *proportional*) when $ab' = a'b$. We use the notation $(a, b) \sim (a', b')$ to express this fact.

The following properties are very easy to check.

*Reflexive property.* $(a, b) \sim (a, b)$ for every ordered pair $(a, b)$.

*Symmetric property.* If $(a, b) \sim (a', b')$, then $(a', b') \sim (a, b)$.

*Transitive property.* If $(a, b) \sim (a', b')$ and $(a', b') \sim (a'', b'')$, then $(a, b) \sim (a'', b'')$.

The set $S$ of ordered pairs of integers (with the second term different from 0) may be organized into *classes of equivalent or proportional pairs* as follows.

For every ordered pair $(a, b) \in S$ we denote by $\dfrac{a}{b}$ (or also $a/b$) the set of all ordered pairs $(a', b') \in S$ such that $(a, b) \sim (a', b')$.

These properties have the following implications.

If $(a, b) \in S$, then $(a, b) \in a/b$.

If $(a', b') \in a/b$, then $(a, b) \in a'/b'$.

If $(a, b)$, $(a', b') \in S$, then either the sets $a/b$, $a'/b'$ coincide or there is no ordered pair in $S$ belonging to both $a/b$ and $a'/b'$.

Therefore, these equivalence classes of ordered pairs are sets of couples such that (*1*) either they have one ordered pair in common, and then, necessarily, all couples from one set are in the other and conversely, or (2) they have no ordered pair in common.

A *rational number* (or a fraction) is an equivalence class of ordered pairs of integers, with the second term distinct from 0.

Two rational numbers $a/b$, $a'/b'$ are said to be *equal*, and we write $a/b = a'/b'$, whenever the equivalence classes $a/b$, $a'/b'$ coincide. Otherwise, we say that $a/b$ and $a'/b'$ are distinct, and we write $a/b \neq a'/b'$. Therefore, $a/b = a'/b'$ exactly when $ab' = a'b$.

The next step is to define the operations between rational numbers.

*Addition of rational numbers:*

$$\frac{a}{b} + \frac{c}{d} = \frac{ad + bc}{bd}$$

This is a natural definition, since

$$\frac{a}{b} = \frac{ad}{bd}, \quad \frac{c}{d} = \frac{bc}{bd},$$

thus nothing is more obvious than to define

$$\frac{a}{b} + \frac{c}{d} = \frac{ad}{bd} + \frac{bc}{bd} = \frac{ad + bc}{bd}.$$

As it stands, this prescription for the definition of sum, no matter how natural, is not yet completely justified. In fact, we must show that if

$$\frac{a}{b} = \frac{a'}{b'}, \quad \frac{c}{d} = \frac{c'}{d'}$$

then

$$\frac{ad + bc}{bd} = \frac{a'd' + b'c'}{b'd'}.$$

In other words, this means that whatever be the ordered pairs $(a, b)$, $(a', b')$ in the equivalence class $a/b$, and $(c, d)$, $(c', d')$ in the equivalence class $c/d$, the ordered pairs $(ad + bc, bd)$, $(a'd' + b'c', b'd')$ belong to the same equivalence class, thus defining the same rational number. Of course, this verification is very easy, since it amounts to the equality $b'd'(ad + bc) = bd(a'd' + b'c')$, which follows from $ab' = ba'$, $cd' = dc'$.

*Multiplication of rational numbers:*

$$\frac{a}{b} \cdot \frac{c}{d} = \frac{ac}{bd}$$

The justification of this rule results from the fact that if

$$\frac{a}{b} = \frac{a'}{b'}, \quad \frac{c}{d} = \frac{c'}{d'}$$

then

$$\frac{ac}{bd} = \frac{a'c'}{b'd'}.$$

We may safely assume that most of us are familiar with the easy task of establishing that the common rules of operations with integers are still valid among rational numbers.

By creating the rational numbers, we have enlarged the set of integers, as explained below.

To every integer we may associate the rational number $a/1$. The operations performed on the rational numbers of this type are the exact counterpart of the similar operations with integers:

$$\frac{a}{1} + \frac{b}{1} = \frac{a+b}{1}, \quad \frac{a}{1} \cdot \frac{b}{1} = \frac{ab}{1}, \quad \text{etc.}$$

Thus, from the *operational point of view*, there is no need to distinguish between the integers $a$ and the corresponding rational numbers $a/1$. However, it must be emphasized that, while $a$ is an integer, $a/1$ is in fact an equivalence class of ordered pairs (among which there is $(a, 1)$).

Since we are interested in the operational laws with numbers, rather than in their nature, it is allowable to think of any integer $a$ as *identified* with the corresponding rational number $a/1$. In a looser way, we say that the set of integers is *contained* in the set of rational numbers, even though what is meant is that to every integer $a$ there corresponds naturally the rational number $a/1$, this correspondence preserving the operations.

In particular, the integers 0, 1, or their corresponding rational numbers $0/1$, $1/1$, have respectively the properties of the "zero element" and of the "unit":

$$\frac{a}{b} + \frac{0}{1} = \frac{a}{b}, \quad \frac{a}{b} \cdot \frac{1}{1} = \frac{a}{b},$$

for every rational number $\frac{a}{b}$.

It is worthwhile to point out that the flaw in the system of integers, in which division could not always be performed, has now been corrected.

If $\dfrac{a}{b}, \dfrac{c}{d}$ are rational numbers, where $\dfrac{c}{d}$ is not zero, then the rational

number $\dfrac{ad}{bc}$ is the quotient of the division of $\dfrac{a}{b}$ by $\dfrac{c}{d}$ :

$$\frac{c}{d} \cdot \frac{ad}{bc} = \frac{a}{b}.$$

Among all the ordered pairs of nonzero integers $(a, b)$, $(c, d)$, . . . such

that $\dfrac{a}{b} = \dfrac{c}{d} = \ldots$ it is possible to find one, let us say $(a, b)$, with the follow-

ing property: $b$ is larger than 0 and no natural number, other than 1, divides both $b$ and $a$ (or $-a$, in case $a < 0$); in other words, $b$ and $a$ are relatively prime integers.

This may be achieved by factoring out all the prime numbers dividing both terms of the given ordered pair.

If a (nonzero) rational number has been written as $\dfrac{a}{b}$ with $b$ and $a$

(or $-a$) relatively prime integers, we say that it is written in *irreducible form*.

The *inequality of rational numbers* is defined as follows: if $\dfrac{a}{b}, \dfrac{c}{d}$ are rational

numbers (written so that $b > 0$, $d > 0$), we say that $\dfrac{a}{b}$ *is smaller than or equal*

*to* $\dfrac{c}{d}$ $\left(\text{or } \dfrac{c}{d} \text{ is greater than or equal to } \dfrac{a}{b}\right)$ when $ad \leqslant bc$.

When $a/b \neq c/d$ and $a/b \leqslant c/d$, we say that $a/b$ is *strictly smaller* than $c/d$, and we write $a/b < c/d$; we may also say that $c/d$ is *strictly greater* than $a/b$.

As in the case of integers, the rational numbers form a linearly ordered set and the notion of inequality is linked to the addition and multiplication of rational numbers by similar compatibility relations.

However, the linearly ordered set of *strictly* positive rational numbers is not well ordered, since it does not have a smallest element; in fact, no rational number $a/b > 0$ can be the smallest strictly positive rational number, since $a/b > a/2b > 0$.

A little more precise and useful is the following fact: *given any rational number $a/b > 0$, there exists a natural number $N$ such that $0 < 1/N < a/b$.*

In fact, it is sufficient to consider $N$ strictly greater than $b$; then $aN \geqslant N > b$.

It is also customary to define the *absolute value* of a rational number $r$ as being $r$ itself, when $r \geqslant 0$, or $-r$ when $r \leqslant 0$. This concept will play an important role in our later discussion. We denote the absolute value of a rational number $r$ by $|r|$.

The following properties for the absolute value are well known and may be easily proved:

$$|0| = 0; \quad \text{if} \quad |r| = 0 \quad \text{then} \quad r = 0$$
$$|-r| = |r|$$
$$|rs| = |r| \cdot |s|$$
$$|r + s| \leqslant |r| + |s|$$

where $r$, $s$ are rational numbers.

This last property is called the *triangle inequality*, since it admits a generalization that may be interpreted to mean that the length of any one side of a triangle is smaller than or equal to the sum of the lengths of the other two sides.

From this inequality, we deduce that

$$|r - s| \geqslant ||r| - |s||,$$

in other words,

$$-|r - s| \leqslant |r| - |s| \leqslant |r - s|.$$

In fact,

$$|r| = |(r - s) + s| \leqslant |r - s| + |s|$$

hence

$$|r| - |s| \leqslant |r - s|.$$

Similarly,

$$|s| - |r| \leqslant |s - r| = |r - s|,$$

hence

$$-|r - s| \leqslant |r| - |s|.$$

### Representation of Rational Numbers by Points of a Straight Line

Let $L$ be a straight line, $O$ a fixed point in $L$ (called the *origin*), and $u$ a unit of length. Let us give an *orientation* to the line $L$, *choosing* one of the half lines defined by $O$ as *positive*, the other one as *negative*.

To every rational number $r = a/b$ (with $b > 0$) we shall associate the point $P$ of the line $L$ so that the oriented segment $\overline{OP}$ has measure $r$, using the unit of length $u$; that is, $b$ times the segment $\overline{OP}$ has measure $a$. This is a one-to-one correspondence from the set of rational numbers into the set of points of the straight line $L$.

## A Historical Question

Is it true that *all* the points of the line $L$ are obtained as images in the above correspondence? Or, do there exist points in the straight line which *do not* correspond to rational numbers? *

In the latter case, there is the possibility of enlarging the set of rational numbers, introducing new numbers (to be called IRRATIONAL numbers) which may still be represented by points of the line $L$.

The need of introducing new numbers had been already felt by PYTHAGORAS in the following problem.

Let $ABC$ be a triangle such that the angle at $A$ is a right angle, and the sides $\overline{AB}$, $\overline{AC}$ have length 1. Then the length of $\overline{BC}$ satisfies the equation $\overline{BC}^2 = \overline{AB}^2 + \overline{AC}^2 = 2$. If $\overline{BC}$ could be measured by a rational number $a/b$ (already written in irreducible form, with $a$ and $b$ relatively prime), then $a^2/b^2 = 2$, hence $a^2 = 2b^2$. Thus, $a^2$ is even and therefore $a$ is even; that is, $a = 2a'$, where $a'$ is an integer. Hence, $a^2 = (2a')^2 = 4a'^2 = 2b^2$ and $b^2 = 2a'^2$. It follows that $b$ is even; consequently $a$, $b$ are not relatively prime, which is a contradiction.

This indicates that the length of $\overline{BC}$ is not a rational number.

Therefore, if we wish to express the length of any segment by means of a "number," we must enlarge the concept of number, adding new numbers to the set of rational numbers. We shall do this in the next chapter.

### Exercises

1. *Construction of the natural numbers.* In this exercise we present the axiomatic definition of the natural numbers, as done by PEANO. Our purpose is to show that it is possible to introduce the natural numbers, on which our work has been based, in an axiomatic way.†

Let $N$ be a set of elements, called *natural numbers*, satisfying the following axioms.

(a) There exists a natural number, denoted by 1.
(b) With every natural number $a$ there is associated a natural number $s(a)$, called the *successor of $a$*.
(c) There exists no natural number $a$ such that $s(a) = 1$.

---

* Here we are considering the straight line in a very naive way. We shall make a more definite comment about it later (p. 29).

† Most likely, the completion of these theoretical exercises, and the similar sets that are to follow, will require a great deal of time and, possibly, some competent guidance.

(d) If $a$, $b$ are natural numbers and $s(a) = s(b)$, then $a = b$.

(e) *Principle of finite induction.* Let $S$ be a set of natural numbers, such that
$1 \in S$ and
if $a \in S$, then $s(a) \in S$;
then every natural number is in $S$.

We define the operation of *addition* of natural numbers as follows. If $a \in N$, we put $a + 1 = s(a)$; if $b \in N$ and $a + b$ has been already defined, we put $a + s(b) = s(a + b)$. (Note, by the principle of finite induction, that $a + b$ is therefore defined for every couple of natural numbers $a$, $b$.)

We define the operation of *multiplication* of natural numbers as follows. If $a \in N$, we put $a.1 = a$; if $b \in N$ and $a.b$ has been already defined, we put $a.s(b) = a.b + a$. (Note again, by the principle of finite induction, that $a.b$ is therefore defined for every couple of natural numbers $a$, $b$).

Prove the following properties of the addition.

Associative law:  $a + (b + c) = (a + b) + c$
Commutative law: $a + b = b + a$
Cancellation law:  if $a + b = a + c$, then $b = c$

Prove the following properties of multiplication.

Associative law:  $a.(b.c) = (a.b).c$
Commutative law: $a.b = b.a$
Cancellation law:  if $a.b = a.c$, then $b = c$
Existence of unit:  for every natural number $a$, we have $a.1$
$= 1.a = a$

Prove also the following distributive laws.

$$a.(b + c) = a.b + a.c, \quad (a + b).c = a.c + b.c$$

Consider the set of natural numbers of the form $1$, $s(1)$, $s(s(1))$, $s(s(s(1)))$, ..., obtained from 1 by taking its iterated successors. Prove, by the principle of finite induction, that every natural number belongs to this set.

Denote the elements of this set respectively by 1, 2, 3, 4, . . . .

We define the *inequality* of natural numbers as follows: $a < b$ when there exists a natural number $c$ such that $a + c = b$. We write $a \leqslant b$ when $a < b$ or $a = b$.

Prove the following properties for the inequality.

Reflexive property:           $a \leqslant a$, but $a < a$ is false
Antisymmetric property:  $a \leqslant b$ and $b \leqslant a$ imply $a = b$
Transitive property:           if $a \leqslant b$ and $b \leqslant c$, then $a \leqslant c$
Linear property:                if $a$, $b \in N$ then either $a \leqslant b$ or $b \leqslant a$
Compatibility property:   if $a$, $b$, $c \in N$ and $a \leqslant b$ then $a + c \leqslant b + c$
and also $a.c \leqslant b.c$

2. *Construction of the integers.* In this exercise, we present the axiomatic definition of integers.

Consider the set of ordered pairs $(a, b)$ of natural numbers. We say that $(a, b)$, $(a', b')$ are equivalent pairs, and we write $(a, b) \equiv (a', b')$ when $a + b' = a' + b$.

Show that the following properties are verified.

Reflexive property:    $(a, b) \equiv (a, b)$
Symmetric property: if $(a, b) \equiv (a', b')$ then $(a', b') \equiv (a, b)$
Transitive property:  if  $(a, b) \equiv (a', b')$  and  $(a', b') \equiv (a'', b'')$
                       then $(a, b) \equiv (a'', b'')$

Therefore, the set of pairs may be organized into classes of equivalent pairs; two pairs are in the same class if and only if they are equivalent.

Let $Z$ denote the set of all equivalent classes of pairs defined as above; each element of $Z$ is called an *integer*.

We define the operation of *addition* of integers as follows: if $m, n \in Z$, let $(a, b)$ be a pair in the equivalence class $m$, and $(c, d)$ a pair in the equivalence class $n$; we define $m + n$ as being the equivalence class of the pair $(a + c, b + d)$.

In order to accept this definition, we have to check that if $(a', b') \equiv (a, b)$, $(c', d') \equiv (c, d)$ then $(a' + c', b' + d') \equiv (a + c, b + d)$; therefore, the addition of elements $m, n$ will not depend on the particular pairs chosen in each of the equivalence classes $m, n$.

We define the operation of *multiplication* of integers as follows: if $m$, $n \in Z$, if $(a, b)$ belongs to the equivalence class $m$, if $(c, d)$ belongs to the equivalence class $n$, we define $m.n$ as being the equivalence class of the pair $(a.c + b.d, b.c + a.d)$. Again, in order to justify this definition, we have to check that if $(a', b') \equiv (a, b)$, $(c', d') \equiv (c, d)$ then

$$(a'.c' + b'.d', b'.c' + a'.d') \equiv (a.c + b.d, b.c + a.d);$$

therefore, the multiplication of elements $m, n$ does not depend on the particular pairs chosen in each of the equivalence classes $m, n$.

Prove the following properties of addition.

Associative law:    $m + (n + p) = (m + n) + p$
Commutative law: $m + n = n + m$
Existence of *zero*:    all the pairs of type $(a, a)$ are equivalent and their class is called the zero, denoted 0; we have $m + 0 = 0 + m = m$, for every $m \in Z$.
Existence of *symmetric:*    for every element $m \in Z$ there exists an element $m' \in Z$ such that $m + m' = m' + m = 0$; $m'$ is uniquely defined with this property.

Prove the following properties of multiplication.

Associative law:    $m.(n.p) = (m.n).p$

Commutative law: $m.n = n.m$

Cancellation law:    if $m$, $n$, $p \in \mathcal{Z}$, $p \neq 0$, and $m.p = n.p$ then $m = n$

Existence of unit:    all the pairs of type $(a + 1, a)$ are equivalent and their class is called the unit element, denoted temporarily by $e$: $e.m = m.e = m$ for every $m \in \mathcal{Z}$

Prove also the following distributive law.

$$m.(n + p) = m.n + m.p, \; (m + n).p = m.p + n.p$$

Next, we consider the following *embedding of the set of natural numbers into the set of integers*. Let $\varphi$ be the correspondence that to every natural number $a$ associates the equivalence class of pairs $(a + 1, 1)$. Prove that $\varphi$ is a one-to-one correspondence from $N$ into $\mathcal{Z}$, such that $\varphi(a + b) = \varphi(a) + \varphi(b)$, $\varphi(a.b) = \varphi(a).\varphi(b)$; moreover, $\varphi(1) = e$ (equivalence class of $(1 + 1, 1)$).

It is customary to identify the natural numbers with their images in $\mathcal{Z}$, by means of the correspondence $\varphi$. Therefore, we may say that every natural number is an integer, in particular, the unit integer $e$ is identified to the natural number 1.

In the set of integers, we define the operation of *subtraction* as follows: if $m$, $n \in \mathcal{Z}$, we show that there exists a unique integer $p \in \mathcal{Z}$ such that $n + p = m$, and we define the *difference m less n* as being equal to $p$; we write $p = m - n$.

For every integer $m$, the symmetric $m'$ of $m$ is equal to $0 - m$, and it is also denoted by $-m$.

Prove that if $a$, $b$ are natural numbers, then $b - a$ is a natural number if and only if $a < b$. Then, the equivalence class of the pair $(a, b)$ of natural numbers is equal to the difference $a - b$ (or, more precisely, to $\varphi(a) - \varphi(b)$).

Next, we define *inequality* between integers as follows: $m < n$ whenever $n - m$ is a natural number, that is, there exists a natural number $p$ such that $m + p = n$. Thus, $n$ is a natural number if and only if $n > 0$. We write $m \leqslant n$ whenever $m = n$ or $m < n$.

Prove the following properties of the inequality of integers.

Reflexive property:    $m \leqslant m$, however $m < m$ is false

Antisymmetric property:    if $m \leqslant n$ and $n \leqslant m$ then $m = n$

Transitive property:    if $m \leqslant n$ and $n \leqslant p$ then $m \leqslant p$

Linear property:    if $m, n \in \mathcal{Z}$ then either $m \leqslant n$ or $n \leqslant m$

Compatibility with
 addition:          if $m, n, p \in \mathcal{Z}$ and $m \leqslant n$ then $m + p \leqslant n + p$

Rule of signs:      $m.(-n) = (-n).m = -(m.n)$, $(-m).(-n) = m.n$

Compatibility with
 multiplication:    if $m, n \in \mathcal{Z}, p \in \mathcal{N}$ and $m < n$ then $m.p < n.p$. Therefore, if $m.n = 0$ then either $m = 0$ or $n = 0$.

The set of all integers is *not* well ordered.

3. *Properties of the rational numbers.* In this exercise we list the most significant properties of operations with rational numbers, which have been defined in the text.

Prove that the addition of rational numbers satisfies the following properties: associative law; commutative law; existence of zero; and existence of symmetric element.

The element symmetric to $a/b$ is denoted by $-a/b$.

The subtraction of rational numbers is defined as

$$\frac{a}{b} - \frac{c}{d} = \frac{a}{b} + \left(-\frac{c}{d}\right).$$

Prove that the multiplication of rational numbers satisfies the following properties: associative law; commutative law; existence of unit element; and existence of inverse: for every rational number $r \neq 0$, there exists a rational number $r'$ such that $r.r' = r'.r = 1$.

Moreover, the distributive laws are verified for rational numbers.

Prove the following rules of signs:

$$r \cdot (-s) = (-r) \cdot s = -(r \cdot s), \quad (-r) \cdot (-s) = r \cdot s,$$

for any rational numbers $r, s$.

Prove the triangle inequality for rational numbers:

$$\left| \frac{a}{b} + \frac{c}{d} \right| \leqslant \left| \frac{a}{b} \right| + \left| \frac{c}{d} \right|$$

4. Show that no rational number has its cube equal to 3.

5. Show that a rational number $a/b$, where $a, b$ are relatively prime integers, is a square of rational number if and only if $a$ and $b$ are squares of integers.

6. A "decimal expansion" $q.a_1a_2 \ldots a_n \ldots$, where $q$ is an integer, $a_1$ are digits $0, 1, 2, \ldots 9$, is said to *terminate* when there exists an index $n_0$ such that $a_n = 0$ for every $n \geqslant n_0$, or else $a_n = 9$, for every $n \geqslant n_0$; it is *periodic* when there exists an index $n_0$ and a natural integer $p \geqslant 1$ such that

$$a_{n_0} = a_{n_0+p} = a_{n_0+2p} = \ldots$$

$$a_{n_0+1} = a_{n_0+1+p} = a_{n_0+1+2p} = \ldots$$

$$\cdots \cdots \cdots \cdots \cdots \cdots \cdots$$

$$a_{n_0+p-1} = a_{n_0+2p-1} = a_{n_0+3p-1} = \ldots$$

Prove that every rational number may be represented by a decimal expansion which terminates or is periodic. (Conversely, it may be proved that every decimal expansion of these types represents a rational number.)

# 3

# Construction of Real Numbers

As we have pointed out, the need for introducing real numbers has been felt since the time of the Greeks. But it was only in the second half of the last century that a first rigorous construction of the real number system was accomplished. At that time a critical study of the foundations of mathematics and the precise formulation of concepts opened the way for the broad horizons of modern mathematics.

CANTOR and DEDEKIND have constructed, independently, the real number system; their methods were distinct but equivalent. We shall present here the essentials of Cantor's construction, omitting the proofs. Dedekind has used the METHOD OF CUTS in his classic memoir (see Appendix A).

The leading idea in Cantor's definition of real numbers is quite simple. If $\overline{OP}$ is a segment whose measure, with respect to the unit of length, is not a rational number, it is possible to find segments of rational length approaching that of $\overline{OP}$ as closely as we may prescribe. This will enable us to identify the length of $\overline{OP}$ with the *sequence of rational lengths* of the segments approximating $\overline{OP}$.

We shall now rigorously examine this idea.

Let $Q$ be the set of rational numbers, assumed to be represented by points of a straight line (those points $P$ such that $\overline{OP}$ has rational length with respect to a unit of length). Let us consider all the infinite sequences $a_1, a_2, \ldots, a_n, \ldots$ of rational numbers, having the following property: *given arbitrarily any integer $N > 0$, the terms of the sequence, with only a finite number of exceptions have a distance to each other less than $1/N$.*

In other words, for every integer $N > 0$, there exists an index $n_0 > 0$ (which depends on $N$, that is, it may have different values for different values of $N$) such that if $m$, $n$ are any indices, $m > n_0$, $n > n_0$, then $|a_m - a_n| < 1/N$.

EXAMPLE OF A SEQUENCE OF THIS TYPE. $a_1 = 3$, $a_2 = 3.1$, $a_3 = 3.14$, $a_4 = 3.141$, $a_5 = 3.1415$, $a_6 = 3.14159 \ldots$ (sequence of rational numbers approaching the number $\pi$). For this sequence,

if we take $N = 10$, then $\quad |a_m - a_n| < \dfrac{1}{10}$ when $m, n > 1$;

if we take $N = 100$, then $\quad |a_m - a_n| < \dfrac{1}{100}$ when $m, n > 2$;

if we take $N = 1000$, then $|a_m - a_n| < \dfrac{1}{1000}$ when $m, n > 3$;

and so on.

It is clear that, given any integer $N$ as large as we like (which is equivalent to having a segment of length $1/N$ as small as we like), all the numbers of the sequence, with at most a finite number of exceptions, lie in some segment of length $1/N$.

ANOTHER EXAMPLE. $a_1 = 1$, $a_2 = 1.2$, $a_3 = 1.3$, $a_4 = 1.4$, $a_5 = 1.41$, $a_6 = 1.413$, $a_7 = 1.4141$, $a_8 = 1.41413, \ldots$ (sequence of rational numbers whose square approaches the number 2). We may verify that this sequence satisfies the property being discussed.

A sequence of this type will be called a FUNDAMENTAL SEQUENCE or a CAUCHY SEQUENCE. In more familiar terms, $a_1, a_2, \ldots, a_n, \ldots$ *is a fundamental sequence when its terms lie in segments as short in length as we like, provided we disregard a finite number of initial terms.*

By this definition, we see at once that if $(a_n)$ is a fundamental sequence and if we disregard or adjoin a *finite* number of initial terms, then the new sequence is still a fundamental sequence.

Fundamental sequences will be used to define the real numbers.

Now we define a NULL SEQUENCE. It is any sequence of rational numbers with the following property: *given arbitrarily any integer $N > 0$, then the terms of the sequence, with only a finite number of exceptions, have absolute value less than* $1/N$.

Thus, given $N$, and disregarding a convenient number of initial terms of the sequence, the remaining terms of the sequence have absolute value less than $1/N$.

For example, the sequence $\dfrac{1}{2}, \dfrac{1}{4}, \dfrac{1}{8}, \ldots, \dfrac{1}{2^n}, \cdots$ is a null sequence. Indeed, given for example $N = 1000$, since $2^{10} = 1024 > 1000$, then $\dfrac{1}{2^{10}} < \dfrac{1}{1000}$ and, therefore, $\dfrac{1}{2^n} < \dfrac{1}{1000}$ as soon as $n \geqslant 10$. The same argument holds for every other $N$.

We point out that it is quite natural not to distinguish between two fundamental sequences $(a_n)$, $(b_n)$, when the sequence of differences $a_1 - b_1$, $a_2 - b_2, \ldots, a_n - b_n, \ldots$ is a null sequence.

The identification of the sequences $(a_n)$ and $(b_n)$ means that their corresponding terms are arbitrarily near, provided that we disregard a finite number of initial terms. We shall say that they are two EQUIVALENT fundamental sequences, and we write $(a_n) \sim (b_n)$.

Precisely, it means that given any integer $N > 0$ there exists an index $n_1$ (which may vary for different values of $N$), such that if $n \geqslant n_1$ then $|a_n - b_n| < 1/N$.

Thus, we may organize the set of fundamental sequences into classes, putting two sequences in the same class when and only when they are equivalent. Such a classification is possible, since the equivalence of fundamental sequences satisfies the following properties (already discussed on page 12, for the equivalence of ordered pairs of integers).

*Reflexive property.* $(a_n) \sim (a_n)$.

*Symmetric property.* If $(a_n) \sim (b_n)$, then $(b_n) \sim (a_n)$.

*Transitive property.* If $(a_n) \sim (b_n)$ and $(b_n) \sim (c_n)$, then $(a_n) \sim (c_n)$.

We are now able to define REAL NUMBER.

DEFINITION. *A real number is a class of equivalent fundamental sequences of rational numbers, in the above sense.*

In other words:

Each fundamental sequence of rational numbers defines a real number. Two fundamental sequences define the same real number if and only if they are equivalent.

We shall now study the real numbers, determining their properties.

*Every Rational Number May Be Considered as a Real Number.*

For, if $a/b$, is the given rational number, then the sequence $a/b$, $a/b$, $a/b, \ldots$ of terms equal to $a/b$, is a fundamental sequence. The real number defined by this sequence is considered identical to the rational number $\dfrac{a}{b}$. [*]

Thus, we may say that *the set of real numbers contains the set of rational numbers.*

---

[*] This identification is allowable, since we are mostly interested in the operational properties of the numbers; it has the same nature as the identification made in Chapter 2 between any integer $a$ and the rational number $a/1$.

*There Exist Real Numbers Which Are Not Rational Numbers;*
*They Are Called IRRATIONAL NUMBERS.*

This may be seen as follows. If we express a rational number as a decimal fraction, it is well known that these decimal developments either terminate (for example, 3.2435807000 . . .) or are periodic (for example, 0.23545454 . . .). See Exercise 6 on page 15.

If we imagine a decimal fraction which is not periodical and does not terminate, for example 0.3245676921 . . . (without period, not terminating), it may be defined by the fundamental sequence $\dfrac{3}{10}, \dfrac{32}{100}, \dfrac{324}{1000},$ $\dfrac{3245}{10000}, \cdots$ Thus, this decimal fraction represents a real number which is not a rational number.

In fact, with the theory of TRANSFINITE CARDINAL NUMBERS, conceived by Cantor, we may show that, in a certain sense, the set of rational numbers has infinitely fewer elements than the set of real numbers. We shall not develop this point here but, instead, shall devote Appendix B to a short exposition of these ideas.

*The Preceding Considerations Allow Us to Infer that the Real Numbers*
*May Be Represented by Means of Decimal Fractions.*

This correspondence is one-to-one, provided we exclude the periodic decimal fractions of period 999 . . ., which may be identified to rational numbers having nonperiodic decimal representation (for example, 0.9999 . . . = 1).

### Operations with Real Numbers

We shall now show how to calculate with the newly introduced real numbers. For this purpose, we must define operations between these numbers in such a way that when applied to the rational numbers they will be reduced to the already known operations between rational numbers.

Therefore, we have to *extend* the operations between rational numbers to operations between real numbers; we shall do this by the *method of prolongation by continuity.*

### Addition of Real Numbers

Let $\alpha$, $\beta$ be real numbers defined respectively by the fundamental sequences $(a_n)$, $(b_n)$.

We *define $\alpha + \beta$ as being that real number given by the fundamental sequence* $(a_n + b_n)$.

To justify this definition, we must show that (1) the sequence $(a_n + b_n)$ is, in fact, a fundamental sequence of rational numbers, and (2) that if $(a'_n)$, $(b'_n)$ are fundamental sequences of rational numbers, defining also the real numbers $\alpha$, $\beta$ respectively, the sequences $(a_n + b_n)$ and $(a'_n + b'_n)$ are also equivalent; therefore, both define the same real number.

This last verification may be easily reduced to the fact that *the "sum" of two null sequences is again a null sequence.*

This way of defining the sum of two real numbers corresponds to the following natural idea. As we have seen, to define a real number by means of sequences of rational numbers is the same as giving a sequence of rational numbers which approach the real number with arbitrarily small error. Thus the sums of rational numbers which approach arbitrarily the real numbers $\alpha$, $\beta$ will be (by definition of $\alpha + \beta$) rational numbers approaching arbitrarily the number $\alpha + \beta$.

### Subtraction and Multiplication of Real Numbers

Let $(a_n)$, $(b_n)$ be fundamental sequences of rational numbers, defining respectively the real numbers $\alpha$, $\beta$. Then we *define $\alpha - \beta$ as being the real number given by the fundamental sequence* $(a_n - b_n)$ and, similarly, we *define $\alpha\beta$ as the one given by* $(a_n b_n)$.

These definitions are legitimate as soon as we check the following.

1. $(a_n - b_n)$, $(a_n b_n)$ are fundamental sequences of rational numbers.

2. If $(a'_n)$, $(b'_n)$ are fundamental sequences, respectively equivalent to $(a_n)$, $(b_n)$, then $(a'_n - b'_n)$ is equivalent to $(a_n - b_n)$ and $(a'_n b'_n)$ is equivalent to $(a_n b_n)$.

### Division of Real Numbers

With respect to the *division of real numbers* $\alpha$ by $\beta$, we need to specify that $\beta$ be different from 0. We shall soon prove (cf. page 23) that if $\beta$ is not 0, it may be defined by a fundamental sequence $(b_n)$ of rational numbers, all distinct from 0; clearly, $(b_n)$ will not be a null sequence.

Therefore, if $(a_n)$ is a fundamental sequence of rational numbers defining $\alpha$, we may consider the sequence $(a_n/b_n)$ of rational numbers. It is a fundamental sequence (as it may be proved); the real number defined by this sequence is called the *quotient of $\alpha$ by $\beta$*, and is denoted by $\alpha/\beta$.

All of the operations thus introduced satisfy the common rules of operations that are valid for the rational numbers.

## Inequalities Between Real Numbers

Let $\alpha$, $\beta$ be two real numbers given by the fundamental sequences $(a_n)$, $(b_n)$, respectively. We shall say that $\alpha$ is *strictly greater than* $\beta$ (or $\beta$ is *strictly smaller than* $\alpha$), and shall write $\alpha > \beta$ or $\beta < \alpha$, *when there exist rational numbers $r$, $s$ such that $b_n \leqslant r < s \leqslant a_n$ for every sufficiently large index $n$.*

As it stands, this definition may make no sense, for other fundamental sequences $(a'_n)$, $(b'_n)$ also could serve to define respectively the same real numbers $\alpha$, $\beta$. We must therefore verify that the same property is still true for any such sequences $(a'_n)$, $(b'_n)$, with convenient rational numbers $r'$, $s'$. Let us do this verification as an example.

For this purpose, we consider an integer $N > 0$ such that

$$\frac{1}{N} < \frac{s - r}{2}$$

and we define

$$r' = r + \frac{1}{N}, \quad s' = s - \frac{1}{N};$$

hence $r'$, $s'$ are rational numbers,

$$s' - r' = \left(s - \frac{1}{N}\right) - \left(r + \frac{1}{N}\right) = s - r - \frac{2}{N} > 0.$$

Since $(a_n)$, $(a_n')$ are equivalent fundamental sequences, given the integer $N$, there exists an index $n_1$ such that if $n \geqslant n_1$ then

$$|a'_n - a_n| < \frac{1}{N}.$$

Therefore, as $s \leqslant a_n$ for every sufficiently large index $n$, it follows that

$$s' = s - \frac{1}{N} \leqslant a_n - \frac{1}{N} < a'_n \quad \text{(for $n$ sufficiently large).}$$

In a similar way, we prove the corresponding fact for $(b_n)$, $(b'_n)$ and $r'$.

Note that we have defined the inequality of real numbers by using the inequality relation between rational numbers, already known.

## *The Set of Real Numbers Is Linearly Ordered.*

This means that the inequality of real numbers satisfies the same properties already indicated (page 4) for the inequalities of integers. Moreover, if $\alpha$, $\beta$, $\gamma$ are real numbers, and $\beta < \gamma$, then $\alpha + \beta < \alpha + \gamma$. If $\alpha > 0$, then $\alpha\beta < \alpha\gamma$.

We shall be content to prove that if $\alpha$, $\beta$ are any two real numbers, either $\alpha = \beta$, or $\alpha > \beta$, or $\alpha < \beta$.

It is sufficient to make the proof in the particular case where $\beta = 0$, that is, every real number $\alpha$ is either $\alpha = 0$, or $\alpha > 0$, or $\alpha < 0$.

The general case follows since if $\alpha$, $\beta$ are real numbers, either $\alpha - \beta = 0$, or $\alpha - \beta > 0$, or $\alpha - \beta < 0$, which implies adding $\beta$, respectively, $\alpha = \beta$, or $\alpha > \beta$, or $\alpha < \beta$.

If this proof seems too subtle to be fully understood at this stage, it should be examined again after having become more familiar with these ideas. We point out, however, that the proof is logically independent of any later development.

Thus let $\alpha$ be a real number, given by a fundamental sequence $(a_n)$ of rational numbers. Intuitively, the terms of the sequence $(a_n)$ are closer and closer together the larger the indices considered.

Two things may happen.

*First Case.* It may be that for every integer $N > 0$ there exists an index $n_0$ (which depends on $N$) with the property that for every index $n \geqslant n_0$ we have $|a_n| < 1/N$. This means that, from some index on, the terms of the sequence lie strictly between $-1/N$ and $1/N$; since this is true for every $N$, we have a null sequence which defines the same real number as the sequence $0, 0, 0, \ldots$, that is, $\alpha = 0$.

*Second Case.* It may be that the opposite of the first case happens. That is, there exists an integer $N > 0$ with the property that, no matter how far we consider a term in the sequence $(a_n)$, another term exists which does not lie strictly between $-1/N$ and $1/N$. Precisely, there exists an integer $N > 0$ such that for *every* index $n$ another index $n_1$ exists, $n_1 \geqslant n$, so that

$$|a_{n_1}| \geqslant \frac{1}{N}.$$

Now we recall that $(a_n)$ is a fundamental sequence. Therefore, given the integer $2N$, there exists an index $n_0$ such that any terms $a_p$, $a_m$, with $p, m \geqslant n_0$ satisfy

$$|a_p - a_m| < \frac{1}{2N}.$$

We may combine these two informations to conclude that, using $n = n_0$, $p = n_1$, not only

$$|a_{n_1}| \geqslant \frac{1}{N} > \frac{1}{2N}$$

but also

$$|a_m| > \frac{1}{2N},$$

for every index $m \geqslant n_0$. Indeed,

$$|a_m| = |a_{n_1} - (a_{n_1} - a_m)| \geqslant |a_{n_1}| - |a_{n_1} - a_m| > \frac{1}{N} - \frac{1}{2N} = \frac{1}{2N}.$$

That is now our situation: some integer $N$ exists, for which $|a_m| > 1/2N$, provided $m \geqslant n_0$. This does not yet tell us that all $a_m$ are positive, or that all $a_m$ are negative (for $m \geqslant n_0$). But this is indeed the case, since if some $a_p$, $a_m$ satisfy

$$a_p < -\frac{1}{2N} < 0 < \frac{1}{2N} < a_m \quad (\text{with } p,\, m \geqslant n_0)$$

then

$$|a_m - a_p| > \frac{1}{N},$$

against the fact that $(a_n)$ is a fundamental sequence.

Thus, either $a_m > 1/2N$ for every sufficiently large index — which implies that $\alpha > 0$ (using $r = 0$, $s = 1/2N$ in the definition of inequality), or $a_m < -1/2N$, for every sufficiently large index — which implies that $\alpha < 0$.

Here is an immediate consequence of the above property: *if $\beta$ is a real number different from zero, it may be defined by a Cauchy sequence $(b_n)$ of rational numbers all different from 0.*

In fact, by hypothesis, $\beta \neq 0$, thus either $\beta > 0$ or $\beta < 0$; therefore, there exists a rational number $r > 0$ such that $|b_n| \geqslant r$ for every sufficiently large index $n$, where $(b_n)$ is a fundamental sequence defining the real number $\beta$. Hence, disregarding a finite number of initial terms, we have a Cauchy sequence defining $\beta$, with the property stated.

Consequently the definition of the *inverse $1/\beta$* of every real number $\beta \neq 0$ is now justified. It follows that:

*If $\alpha$, $\beta$ are real numbers and $\alpha\beta = 0$ then either $\alpha = 0$ or $\beta = 0$.*

The reason is that if $\beta \neq 0$, it has an inverse $\beta^{-1}$, and thus $0 = 0.\beta^{-1} = (\alpha\beta).\beta^{-1} = \alpha.(\beta.\beta^{-1}) = \alpha.1 = \alpha$.

It is also an immediate consequence of the definition that *if $\alpha$, $\beta$ are any two real numbers such that $\beta < \alpha$, there exists a rational number $r$ in between:* $\beta < r < \alpha$.

We describe this situation by saying that *the rational numbers are densely distributed among the real numbers.*

It follows that *given any real number $\alpha > 0$, there exists an integer $N$ so large that $0 < 1/N < \alpha$.*

We need only to notice that a rational number $r$ lies between 0 and $\alpha$, and some fraction $1/N$ is smaller than $r$, as was shown on page 8.

More generally, the real numbers satisfy the following *archimedean property*.

*If $\alpha$, $\beta$ are any strictly positive real numbers, there exists an integer $N$ such that $N\alpha > \beta$.*

In fact, since $\beta > 0$, the quotient $\alpha/\beta$ exists and $\alpha/\beta > 0$; thus there exists an integer $N$ for which $1/N < \alpha/\beta$, hence $\beta < N\alpha$.

### Absolute Value of a Real Number

We define the absolute value $|\alpha|$ of the real number $\alpha$ as follows:

$$|\alpha| = \alpha \text{ when } \alpha \geqslant 0, \text{ and } |\alpha| = -\alpha \text{ when } \alpha \leqslant 0.$$

The absolute value of real numbers satisfies the same properties as in the case of rational numbers.

Especially important is the triangle inequality: $|\alpha + \beta| \leqslant |\alpha| + |\beta|$ for any real numbers $\alpha$, $\beta$.

We may use this definition to express the following property.

*If $(a_n)$ is a fundamental sequence of rational numbers defining the real number $\alpha$, then, given arbitrarily an integer $N > 0$, there exists a convenient index $n_0$ such that, for every index $n \geqslant n_0$, we have*

$$|\alpha - a_n| \leqslant \frac{1}{N}.$$

Indeed, since $(a_n)$ is a fundamental sequence, given the integer $N$, there exists an index $n_0$ such that, if $m \geqslant n_0$, $n \geqslant n_0$, then

$$|a_m - a_n| < \frac{1}{N}.$$

Let us fix an arbitrary index $n$, $n \geqslant n_0$, and consider these two sequences:

$$a_1, a_2, a_3, \ldots, a_m, \ldots$$

and

$$a_n, a_n, a_n, \ldots, a_n, \ldots$$

(all its terms equal to $a_n$). They define respectively the real numbers $\alpha$, $a_n$, so the sequence

$$a_1 - a_n, a_2 - a_n, a_3 - a_n, \ldots, a_m - a_n, \ldots$$

defines $\alpha - a_n$. Since

$$-\frac{1}{N} < a_m - a_n < \frac{1}{N}$$

for every index $m \geqslant n_0$, the real number $\alpha - a_n$ satisfies also

$$-\frac{1}{N} \leqslant \alpha - a_n \leqslant \frac{1}{N}$$

(using simple properties of inequalities between real numbers), that is,

$$|\alpha - a_n| \leqslant \frac{1}{N}.$$

This holds for every index $n \geqslant n_0$.

## Powers of Real Numbers with Rational Exponents

Let $\alpha$ be a real number, $n > 0$ an integer. We define $\alpha^n$ (*n*th power of $\alpha$) as the product of $n$ numbers equal to $\alpha$:

$$\alpha^n = \alpha.\alpha \ldots \alpha \ (n \text{ times}).$$

Thus

$$\alpha^1 = \alpha, \quad \alpha^2 = \alpha.\alpha, \quad \alpha^3 = \alpha.\alpha.\alpha,$$

and so on.

Therefore,

$$\alpha^m.\alpha^n = \alpha^{m+n}, \quad \alpha^{m.n} = (\alpha^m)^n,$$

for any integers $m, n > 0$. Also, if $\alpha \neq 0$, then $\alpha^n \neq 0$.

Next, we shall give a meaning to $\alpha^n$, where $\alpha \neq 0$ and $n$ is an integer, $n \leqslant 0$. If we intend to have the above property $\alpha^m.\alpha^n = \alpha^{m+n}$ valid also when $m \leqslant 0, n \leqslant 0$, the definition of $\alpha^0$ must be such that $\alpha.\alpha^0 = \alpha$ (using $m = 1, n = 0$), hence necessarily $\alpha^0 = 1$; in the same way (using $m = -n$), $\alpha^{-n}.\alpha^n = \alpha^0 = 1$, and thus $\alpha^{-n} = 1/\alpha^n$ (note that $\alpha^n \neq 0$ since $\alpha \neq 0$).

Thus, we actually define $\alpha^0 = 1$, $\alpha^{-n} = 1/\alpha^n$, and it is now easy to verify that the above rules are still valid when $m, n$ are any integers.

It is also evident that if $\alpha, \beta$ are real numbers, $n$ any integer, $n \neq 0$, then $\alpha^n = \beta^n$ imply $\alpha = \beta$. Indeed, taking the inverses, the case where $n < 0$ is reduced to the one with $n \geqslant 1$, which we may prove by induction on $n$, using the fact that the set of real numbers is linearly ordered.

If we try now to define $\alpha^{1/q}$ where $\alpha > 0$ and $q > 0$ is an integer, we shall be required to perform certain computations that are rather tedious. Indeed, we want to find a fundamental sequence $(r_n)$ of rational numbers such that, calling $a_n = r_n{}^q$, then $(a_n)$ is a fundamental sequence defining the real number $\alpha$. Moreover, we have to remark that if $(r_n')$ is another sequence with the same property as $(r_n)$, then they are equivalent sequences and, therefore, they define the same real number $\beta$. We define, $\beta = \alpha^{1/q}$, and we may also use the notation $\sqrt[q]{\alpha}$ (or $\sqrt{\alpha}$, when $q = 2$).

Rather than break continuity, we postpone these explicit computations to the end of this section. They are included as a representative example of the kind of manipulations that we may have to perform. However, it will be a remarkable improvement when, in Chapter 8, we show that these computations may be avoided by the use of the theory to be developed. Thus, we shall return to the subject on different occasions, since we may consider the study of powers of real numbers as a touchstone for the applications of our theory.

Granted that the definition of $\beta = \alpha^{1/q}$ (where $\alpha > 0$, $q > 0$ is an integer) has been justified, it implies that $\beta^q = (\alpha^{1/q})^q = \alpha$; in particular, $\alpha^{1/q} \neq 0$. Indeed, $(r_n)$ is a fundamental sequence defining $\alpha^{1/q}$ exactly when $(r_n{}^q)$ is a fundamental sequence defining $\alpha$; but $(r_n{}^q)$ defines also $(\alpha^{1/q})^q$ (by definition of multiplication of real numbers), and thus $(\alpha^{1/q})^q = \alpha$.

Similarly, if $p$ is any integer and $\alpha$, $q$ are as before, then $(\alpha^p)^{1/q} = (\alpha^{1/q})^p$. A similar proof for this fact is not very difficult.

Next, if $\alpha > 0$, $q > 0$, we define $\alpha^{-1/q} = 1/\alpha^{1/q}$.

Finally, if $\alpha > 0$, $p$, $q$ are integers, $q > 0$, then we define $\alpha^{p/q} = (\alpha^{1/q})^p$.

This definition cannot be accepted without further justification. In fact, if $r$ is a rational number and $r = p/q = p'/q'$, with $q > 0$, $q' > 0$, it has not yet been proved that $(\alpha^{1/q})^p = (\alpha^{1/q'})^{p'}$. But this is true: let $\beta = (\alpha^{1/q})^p$, $\beta' = (\alpha^{1/q'})^{p'}$, so $\beta^{qq'} = ((\alpha^{1/q})^p)^{qq'} = ((\alpha^p)^{1/q})^{qq'} = \alpha^{pq'}$, and similarly, $\beta'^{qq'} = \alpha^{p'q}$; from $pq' = p'q$ it follows that $\beta^{qq'} = \beta'^{qq'}$, therefore $\beta = \beta'$.

The same computation laws, which are known for the powers of rational numbers, are still valid:

$$(\alpha^{p/q})^{r/s} = \alpha^{pr/qs}, \quad (\alpha.\beta)^{p/q} = (\alpha^{p/q}).(\beta^{p/q}),$$

$$(\alpha^{p/q}).(\alpha^{r/s}) = \alpha^{p/q+r/s},$$

where $\alpha > 0$, $\beta > 0$ and $p/q$, $r/s$ are rational numbers.

Note that the symbol $\alpha^{p/q}$ is not defined in all cases.

1. If $\alpha = 0$, $p/q = 0$, then $0^0$ has not been defined.
2. If $\alpha = 0$, $p/q < 0$, then $0^{p/q}$ has not been defined.
3. If $\alpha^p < 0$ and $|q|$ is even, then $\alpha^{p/q}$ has not been defined.

In this last case, for example, the symbol $(-1)^{1/2}$ is included. If we want to interpret this symbol (in other words, if the result of this operation should be a "number"), we must extend again the notion of real number to a wider class. In fact, it is impossible to find any real number $\beta$ such that $(-1)^{1/2} = \beta$, that is, $-1 = \beta^2$, for the square of any real number is positive or zero. These considerations would lead to the introduction of the COMPLEX NUMBERS, but this will not be done in this book.

**Computations Required for the Definition of $\alpha^{1/q}$,
where $\alpha > 0$ and q is an Integer, q $> 1$**

1. *Determination of a Sequence $(r_n)$ of Rational Numbers such that $(r_n{}^q)$ is a Fundamental Sequence defining $\alpha$.* It is enough to find, for every sufficiently large integer $n > 0$ (for which $1/n < \alpha$), a rational number $r_n = b_n/c_n$ such that

$$\alpha - \frac{1}{n} < \frac{b_n{}^q}{c_n{}^q} < \alpha + \frac{1}{n}.$$

Thus we are reduced to proving that *between any two distinct strictly positive real numbers there exists a qth power of a rational number* (where $q$ is a given natural number).

Given the real numbers $\beta$, $\gamma$, $\beta < \gamma$, we see, intuitively, that we have to choose a rational number with such a large denominator $c > 0$ that the following cannot be true:

$$\left(\frac{a}{c}\right)^q < \beta < \gamma < \left(\frac{a+1}{c}\right)^q \tag{1}$$

Actually these inequalities would imply (using the NEWTON binomial formula) that

$$c^q(\gamma - \beta) < (a+1)^q - a^q = \binom{q}{1}a^{q-1} + \binom{q}{2}a^{q-2} + \ldots + 1$$

Let $k$ be the largest of the integers $\binom{q}{1}$, $\binom{q}{2}$, $\ldots$; since $1 \leqslant a \leqslant a^2 \leqslant \ldots \leqslant a^{q-1}$, this relation implies that

$$c^q(\gamma - \beta) < kqa^{q-1}$$

hence

$$c^{q^2}(\gamma - \beta)^q < k^q q^q a^{q(q-1)}.$$

Therefore, since $a^q < c^q\beta$, then

$$c^{q^2}(\gamma - \beta)^q < k^q q^q c^{q(q-1)}\beta^{q-1},$$

$$c^q < \left(\frac{kq}{\gamma - \beta}\right)^q \beta^{q-1}$$

The right-hand side is a real number which depends only on $\beta$, $\gamma$, and $q$. By choosing $c$ so large that

$$c^q \geqslant \left(\frac{kq}{\gamma - \beta}\right)^q \beta^{q-1}$$

we see that the inequalities (eq. 1) cannot be verified, as we had to prove.

2. *Verification that if $(r_n)$ is a Sequence of Rational Numbers such that $(r_n{}^q)$ is a Fundamental Sequence, then $(r_n)$ is itself a Fundamental Sequence.* As we know, we may drop at will a finite number of terms in a fundamental sequence, obtaining still a fundamental sequence. It is convenient in our case to choose an integer $M$ so large that $\dfrac{1}{M} < \alpha$ and disregard the finite number of initial terms of the fundamental sequence $(r_n{}^q)$ defining $\alpha$, such that

$$r_n{}^q < \alpha - \frac{1}{M}.$$

Next we notice that if $M'$ is an integer such that

$$M'^q > \frac{1}{\alpha - \dfrac{1}{M}}$$

then

$$r_n > \frac{1}{M'},$$

for every index $n$.

Now, given a natural number $N$, there exists another $N'$ so large that

$$\frac{1}{N'} \cdot \frac{M'^{q-1}}{q} < \frac{1}{N},$$

that is,

$$N' > \frac{N M'^{q-1}}{q}.$$

Since $(r_n{}^q)$ is a fundamental sequence, associated with $N'$, there exists an index $n_0$ such that if $m, n \geqq n_0$ then

$$|r_m{}^q - r_n{}^q| < \frac{1}{N'}.$$

But

$$|r_m - r_n| = \frac{|r_m{}^q - r_n{}^q|}{|r_m^{q-1} + r_m^{q-2} \cdot r_n + \ldots + r_m \cdot r_n^{q-2} + r_n^{q-1}|},$$

$$|r_m^{q-1} + r_m^{q-2} \cdot r_n + \ldots + r_m \cdot r_n^{q-2} + r_n^{q-1}| > q \cdot \left(\frac{1}{M'}\right)^{q-1};$$

thus, if $m, n \geqq n_0$, then

$$|r_m - r_n| < \frac{1}{N'} \cdot \frac{M'^{q-1}}{q} < \frac{1}{N}.$$

This shows that $(r_n)$ is a fundamental sequence.

3. *Verification that if* $(r_n)$, $(r'_n)$ *are Sequences of Rational Numbers such that* $(r_n{}^q)$, $(r'_n{}^q)$ *are Fundamental Sequences defining the same Real Number* $\alpha$, *then* $(r_n)$, $(r'_n)$ *are also Equivalent Fundamental Sequences.*

The proof, quite similar to the preceding one, may be omitted here.

### Identification of the Set of Real Numbers with the Points of a Straight Line

We know already that if $L$ is a straight line with a positive orientation, if 0 is a fixed point in $L$, and if $u$ is a unit of length, then it is possible to represent every rational number $r$ by means of some point $P$ of $L$, in such a way that the oriented segment $\overline{OP}$ has length given by the rational number $r$.

Since every segment $\overline{OP}$ may be approached, as closely as we like, by segments with rational length, it is natural to conceive the straight line $L$ as being composed of two different types of points: (*1*) the "rational points" $P$, for which the length of $\overline{OP}$ is measured by a rational number; and (*2*) the "irrational points" $P$, for which the length of $\overline{OP}$ is measured by an irrational number.

Summarizing, these have been the steps in identifying the real numbers with the points of a straight line.

1. The rational numbers are known and may be represented by points of the line $L$ (see page 9).

2. These rational points cannot be *all* the points in $L$ (see page 10).

3. Next we construct the real numbers, which are either rational or irrational, and we extend by continuity the operations between rational numbers to operations between real numbers.

4. At this point, we have a precise knowledge of the set of real numbers, while our idea of the straight line is somewhat indefinite, based on our intuition; therefore, it is natural to conceive the straight line as a perfect image or copy of the set of real numbers (by a one-to-one and onto correspondence).\*

Thus, *real number* and *point of a line* may be used in equivalent ways.

### The Symbols $+\infty$ and $-\infty$

It is convenient to adjoin to the set of real numbers two new symbols, denoted $+\infty$, $-\infty$ and called PLUS INFINITY, MINUS INFINITY. These

---

\* A more serious reason will be considered later: We may repeat Cantor's construction, starting with the real numbers. But Cauchy's theorem will assert exactly that to each fundamental sequence of real numbers corresponds one real number — and not a number of any wider class of numbers.

symbols are definitely not real numbers, and we should carefully avoid the mistake of considering them as real numbers. It is sometimes useful, however, to operate with these symbols, as well as to relate them with real numbers.

The following properties are taken as an inherent part of the definition of $+\infty$, $-\infty$ and, of course, are not to be proved.

For every real number $\alpha$,

$$-\infty < \alpha < +\infty$$

$$\alpha + (+\infty) = (+\infty) + \alpha = (+\infty) + (+\infty) = +\infty$$

$$\alpha + (-\infty) = (-\infty) + \alpha = (-\infty) + (-\infty) = -\infty$$

$$\alpha - (-\infty) = (+\infty) - (-\infty) = +\infty$$

$$\alpha - (+\infty) = (-\infty) - (+\infty) = -\infty$$

For every real number $\alpha > 0$,

$$\alpha.(+\infty) = (+\infty).\alpha = (+\infty).(+\infty) = (-\infty).(-\infty) = +\infty$$

$$\alpha.(-\infty) = (-\infty).\alpha = (-\infty).(+\infty) = (+\infty).(-\infty) = -\infty$$

For every real number $\alpha < 0$,

$$\alpha.(+\infty) = (+\infty).\alpha = -\infty$$

$$\alpha.(-\infty) = (-\infty).\alpha = +\infty$$

For every real number $\alpha$,

$$\frac{\alpha}{+\infty} = \frac{\alpha}{-\infty} = 0$$

Expressions such as $(+\infty) - (+\infty)$, $(-\infty) - (-\infty)$, $0.(+\infty)$, $+\infty/+\infty$, and the like, do not make any sense.

The reason for adjoining these symbols $+\infty$, $-\infty$ is purely a matter of convenience, which will be justified in the next chapters.

We may, however, try to give a geometrical motivation for the introduction of $+\infty$, $-\infty$.

As we have seen, the real numbers correspond in one-to-one way to the points of a straight line, and with the definition of inequality, the set of real numbers constitutes a linearly ordered set. However, no real number could be called *the last real number* with this ordering, since no real number is greater than every other; correspondingly, no point of the straight line (drawn horizontally) is more to the right than every other one. On the contrary, given any point of the line, there exist more points at its right; thus we may say that the straight line extends indefinitely to the right (as well as to the left). It may be useful to imagine the straight line completed in such a way as to become closed at the ends, with a point more to the right than any other, the so-called $+\infty$, and a point more to the left than any other, the so-called $-\infty$. We may also say that the farther at the right is a point from the origin, the nearer it is to $+\infty$. The same is true at the other side.

### Exercises

1. *Properties of the real numbers.* In this exercise, we list some of the most significant properties of operations with real numbers, which have been defined in the text.

Prove that the operation of addition of real numbers satisfies the following properties: associative law, commutative law, existence of zero, and existence of symmetric.

The symmetric of the real number $\alpha$ is denoted by $-\alpha$, and it is uniquely defined by $\alpha$.

Define subtraction of real numbers by: $\alpha - \beta = \alpha + (-\beta)$.

Prove that the operation of multiplication of real numbers satisfies the following properties: associative law, commutative law, existence of unit element, and existence of inverse.

Moreover, prove the distributive laws for real numbers.

Prove that $\alpha > \beta$ if and only if $\alpha - \beta > 0$.

The following rules of signs are satisfied:

$$(-\alpha).\beta = \alpha.(-\beta) = -(\alpha.\beta), \quad (-\alpha).(-\beta) = \alpha.\beta.$$

If $\alpha.\beta = 0$ then either $\alpha = 0$ or $\beta = 0$.

Prove that the inequality of real numbers satisfies the following compatibility properties: if $\alpha$, $\beta$, $\gamma$ are real numbers and $\alpha \leqslant \beta$ then $\alpha + \gamma \leqslant \beta + \gamma$; if $\alpha$, $\beta$, $\gamma$ are real numbers, $\alpha < \beta$ and $0 < \gamma$, then $\alpha.\gamma < \beta.\gamma$.

Prove the triangle inequality for real numbers:

$$|\alpha + \beta| \leqslant |\alpha| + |\beta|.$$

2. Show that the sequence $a_0 = 1$, $a_1 = 1.1$, $a_2 = 1.11$, $a_3 = 1.111, \ldots$ is a fundamental or Cauchy sequence.

If $N = 3000$, determine $n_0$ such that if $m, n \geqslant n_0$ then

$$|a_m - a_n| < \frac{1}{3000}.$$

3. Show that the decimal fraction $0.11101010001010\ldots$, in which the $n$th digit in the decimal part is 1 when $n$ is prime, or 0, otherwise, represents an irrational number.

4. Prove the CAUCHY-SCHWARZ inequality:
If

$$a_1, a_2, \ldots, a_n, b_1, b_2, \ldots, b_n$$

are real numbers, then

$$(a_1 b_1 + a_2 b_2 + \ldots + a_n b_n)^2 \leqslant (a_1^2 + \ldots + a_n^2) \cdot (b_1^2 + \ldots + b_n^2).$$

This proof may be accomplished either by direct computation, or by using this fact: consider the polynomial of second degree

$$(a_1 X + b_1)^2 + (a_2 X + b_2)^2 + \ldots + (a_n X + b_n)^2 = AX^2 + BX + C;$$

since its values are nonnegative, for every real number $x$, then

$$B^2 - 4AC \leqslant 0.$$

5. Prove the following MINKOWSKI inequality:
If

$$a_1, a_2, \ldots, a_n, b_1, b_2, \ldots, b_n$$

are real numbers, then

$$\sqrt{(a_1 + b_1)^2 + \ldots + (a_n + b_n)^2} \leqslant \sqrt{a_1^2 + \ldots + a_n^2} + \sqrt{b_1^2 + \ldots + b_n^2}.$$

# 4

# Bounded Sets, Accumulation Points

Now, we shall study the most important properties of the set of real numbers.

We introduce some basic definitions.

Any two real numbers $a$, $b$, such that $a < b$, determine intervals.

CLOSED INTERVAL $[a, b]$. Set of all real numbers $x$ such that $a \leqslant x \leqslant b$.

OPEN INTERVAL $(a, b)$. Set of all real numbers $x$ such that $a < x < b$.

SEMIOPEN INTERVALS. $[a, b)$, set of all real numbers $x$ such that $a \leqslant x < b$; and $(a, b]$, set of all real numbers $x$ such that $a < x \leqslant b$.

Any real number $a$ determines half-lines.

CLOSED HALF-LINES. $[a, +\infty)$, set of all real numbers $x$ such that $a \leqslant x$; and $(-\infty, a]$, set of all real numbers $x$ such that $x \leqslant a$.

OPEN HALF-LINES. $(a, +\infty)$, set of all real numbers $x$ such that $a < x$; and $(-\infty, a)$, set of all real numbers $x$ such that $x < a$.

A set $S$ of real numbers is BOUNDED ABOVE when there exists a real number $a$ such that if $x \in S$ then $x \leqslant a$.

This means that the set $S$ is contained in the half-line $(-\infty, a]$.

A similar definition is given for a set $S$ BOUNDED BELOW: $S$ is contained in some half-line $[a, +\infty)$.

A set $S$ of real numbers is BOUNDED when it is bounded above and below; this means that $S$ is contained in some closed interval $[a, b]$.

EXAMPLES. The following sets are bounded above but not below.

$$S = \{1, 0, -1, -2, -3, \ldots, -n, \ldots\}$$
$$S = (-\infty, 1)$$
$$S = (-\infty, 0)$$

**33**

The following sets are bounded.

$$S = \left\{ 1, \frac{1}{2}, \frac{1}{3}, \ldots, \frac{1}{n}, \ldots \right\};$$

every set which consists of only a finite number of real numbers; every interval $(a, b)$ or $[a, b]$, or semiopen interval; every set obtained as the UNION of a finite number of bounded sets;* and every set which is a part of a bounded set.

The following sets are neither bounded above nor bounded below.

> The whole straight line.
> The set of all rational numbers.
> The set of all integers, positive or negative.

To say that a set $S$ of real numbers is not bounded (that is, $S$ is UN-BOUNDED) means that, given any positive integer $N$, as large as we like, there exists some element $x$ in $S$ such that $|x| > N$.

## ACCUMULATION POINT of a Set

Let $S$ be the set of numbers $\{1, 1/2, 1/3, 1/4, \ldots, 1/n, \ldots\}$. Intuitively, we see that these numbers are *accumulating in the neighborhood of* 0.

Similarly, the real numbers $x$ such that $a \leqslant x \leqslant b$ are accumulating near $a$.

We shall make accurate this idea, by introducing the concept of accumulation point of a set $S$ of real numbers.

Let $S$ be a set of real numbers. A real number $a$ (which may be in $S$ or not in $S$) is called an ACCUMULATION POINT FOR $S$ when, for every positive integer $N$ (as large as we like), there exists at least one point of $S$ different from $a$, and belonging to the open interval $(a - 1/N, a + 1/N)$.

It is the same as saying that each interval $(a - 1/N, a + 1/N)$ has, in common with $S$, at least one point distinct from $a$.

EXAMPLES. 0 is an accumulation point for the set $S = \{1, 1/2, 1/3, \ldots, 1/n, \ldots\}$ because, for example, the interval $(-1/10, 1/10)$ contains the number $1/11$ of $S$; more generally, the interval $(-1/N, 1/N)$ contains the number $1/(N + 1)$ of $S$.

Similarly, $a$ is an accumulation point for $S = [a, b]$, as we may easily verify. In fact, every point of $[a, b]$ is an accumulation point for this set.

---

* If we consider a collection of sets which are parts of a given set $S$, we may form a new set, called the UNION OF THE COLLECTION OF SETS. It consists of all the elements $x \in S$ which belong to at least one of the sets of the given collection.

We may also show that the interval $[a, b]$ is the set of accumulation points for the interval $(a, b)$.

Note that in the definition of an accumulation point $a$ for $S$, we have only required the existence of an element of $S$ (different from $a$) in *each* interval $(a - 1/N, a + 1/N)$. Since this holds true for each such interval, it follows that:

*If $a$ is an accumulation point for the set $S$, then each interval $(a - 1/N$, $a + 1/N)$ contains infinitely many points of $S$.*

*Proof.* If some interval $(a - 1/N, a + 1/N)$ contains only a finite number of points $c_1, \ldots, c_m$ of the set $S$, distinct from $a$, let us consider the numbers $|a - c_1|$, $|a - c_2|, \ldots, |a - c_m|$ ; each of these numbers is strictly positive, since $a$ is distinct from $c_1, \ldots, c_m$. Therefore, we may find a sufficiently large integer $N_1 > 0$, such that

$$\frac{1}{N_1} < |a - c_1|, \ldots, \frac{1}{N_1} < |a - c_m|.$$

Thus, in the interval $(a - 1/N_1, a + 1/N_1)$ there would be no point of $S$, different from $a$, and $a$ could not be an accumulation point for $S$; this is a contradiction.

It follows, from this property, that:

*A finite set of real numbers does not have any accumulation point.*

What about an infinite set? Does there exist an accumulation point for every infinite set?

A simple reflection tells us that this is not a proper question, since its answer is clearly negative: the set $\{1, 2, 3, \ldots, n, \ldots\}$ of all natural integers does not have any accumulation point.

The reason is that, being unbounded, this set of natural integers may contain infinitely many elements, without implying that these points must be close together.

A more sensible question is:

Does there exist an accumulation point for every infinite and bounded set?

The answer is yes, and this constitutes the *fundamental theorem of* BOLZANO *and* WEIERSTRASS:

*Any infinite bounded set of real numbers has at least one accumulation point.*

Let $S$ be an infinite bounded set of real numbers. Thus, $S$ is contained in some closed interval $[a, b]$, where $a$, $b$ are rational numbers, $a < b$. Let $c_1 = (a + b)/2$ be the middle point between $a$ and $b$, and let us consider the intervals $[a, c_1]$ and $[c_1, b]$, halves of $[a, b]$. Since $S$ is an infinite set contained in $[a, b]$, there are infinitely many points of $S$ either in $[a, c_1]$ or in $[c_1, b]$; possibly both intervals $[a, c_1]$ and $[c_1, b]$ contain infinitely many points of $S$.

To develop our proof we are interested in intervals containing infinitely many points of $S$. We select, among the intervals $[a, c_1]$, $[c_1, b]$, the one which contains infinitely many points of $S$, or if both do, we select the right-hand half $[c_1, b]$ of $[a, b]$. And we designate the selected interval by $[a_1, b_1]$, as we are now going to repeat the same argument starting with the interval $[a_1, b_1]$.

We divide $[a_1, b_1]$ at the middle point $c_2$, and notice that at least one of the intervals $[a_1, c_2]$ or $[c_2, b_1]$ contains infinitely many points of $S$; then we choose the one of these intervals containing infinitely many points of $S$ and more to the right, and call it $[a_2, b_2]$.

This process may be repeated indefinitely and, thus, we obtain a sequence $[a, b]$, $[a_1, b_1]$, $[a_2, b_2]$, ..., $[a_n, b_n]$, ..., of intervals, each being one half of the preceding one. We have also

$$a \leq a_1 \leq a_2 \leq \ldots \leq a_n \leq \ldots \leq \ldots b_n \leq \ldots \leq b_2 \leq b_1 \leq b,$$

where all the numbers $a_n$, $b_n$ are rational numbers, since they have been obtained from $a$, $b$ by sums and divisions by 2.

We claim that $(a_n)$, $(b_n)$ are fundamental sequences of rational numbers. Let us show this for the sequence $(a_n)$. Given any integer $N > 0$, no matter how large, it is certain that after a convenient number $n_0$ of subdivisions of $[a, b]$, we obtain intervals $[a_n, b_n]$, whose length is $(b - a)/2^n < 1/N$; it is sufficient to take $n_0$ so large that $2^{n_0} > N(b - a)$. Thus, for $n \geq n_0$, all the points $a_n$ belong to $[a_{n_0}, b_{n_0}]$ and, therefore, if $m \geq n_0$, then

$$|a_m - a_n| \leq b_{n_0} - a_{n_0} = \frac{b - a}{2^{n_0}} < \frac{1}{N}.$$

This means that, disregarding a convenient number of initial terms, all the other terms of the sequence $(a_n)$ concentrate in an interval of length $1/N$; thus, $(a_n)$ is a fundamental sequence. In the same way, we prove that $(b_n)$ is also a fundamental sequence.

Finally, the sequence $(a_n - b_n)$ is a null sequence because the lengths of the intervals $[a_n, b_n]$ ultimately will become arbitrarily small. Therefore, $(a_n)$, $(b_n)$ are equivalent sequences.

This being true, $(a_n)$, $(b_n)$ define one and the same real number $\alpha$. We now show that $\alpha$ is an accumulation point for $S$.

Let $N$ be any given positive integer. Then, for every sufficiently large integer $n$ we have $|\alpha - a_n| < 1/N$ and also $|\alpha - b_n| < 1/N$ (see Chapter 3, p. 24); this means that $\alpha - 1/N < a_n < b_n < \alpha + 1/N$; hence, the interval $(\alpha - 1/N, \alpha + 1/N)$ contains the interval $[a_n, b_n]$ and, therefore, infinitely many points of $S$; since this is true for every integer $N > 0$, it means that $\alpha$ is an accumulation point for $S$.

*Note.* The accumulation point $\alpha$, obtained in the proof of the theorem, satisfies the following property: it is not excluded that there exists an infinite number of elements $x$ in $S$ such that $\alpha < x$; however, *for every integer $N > 0$, there exists only a finite number of elements $x$ in $S$, such that $\alpha + 1/N < x$.*

If this were not the case, there would exist infinitely many elements $x \in S$, $\alpha + 1/N < x$. Considering, in the preceding proof, an interval $[a_n, b_n]$ contained in $(\alpha - 1/N, \alpha + 1/N)$, there would exist infinitely many points $x \in S$, such that $b_n < \alpha + 1/N < x$. Thus, in the subdivision step of the preceding interval $[a_{n-1}, b_{n-1}]$, the half interval $[a_n, b_n]$ is not the one *more to the right* containing infinitely many points of $S$; but this is contrary to the choice of $[a_n, b_n]$.

From this property, it follows:

The accumulation point $\alpha$ for $S$ thus obtained, is the one *farthest to the right,* among the accumulation points of $S$. It is called the LIMIT SUPERIOR of $S$.

Similarly, if $S$ is an infinite bounded set, it contains an accumulation point more to the left, among the accumulation points of $S$. It is called the LIMIT INFERIOR of $S$, and satisfies properties similar to those of the limit superior.

EXAMPLES. Let $S = \{0, 1/2, -1/2, 2/3, -2/3, 3/4, -3/4, \ldots, n/(n+1), -n/(n+1), \ldots\}$. The points $1$, $-1$ do not lie in $S$ but are accumulation points of $S$; they are the only ones. Point $1$ is the limit superior of $S$; point $-1$ is the limit inferior of $S$.

Let $S = [a, b]$; then $a$ is the limit inferior, $b$ is the limit superior of $S$, and every point of $[a, b]$ is an accumulation point for $S$.

DEFINITION OF LEAST UPPER BOUND AND GREATEST LOWER BOUND OF A SET. *Let $S$ be a (nonempty) set of real numbers. The real number $U$ is called the* LEAST UPPER BOUND *or* SUPREMUM *of $S$ whenever it satisfies the following two properties.*

1. $U \geq x$ for every $x$ in $S$.

2. For every positive integer $N$ there exists at least one element $x$ in $S$ such that $U - 1/N < x$.

From this definition it does not follow that $U$ must belong to $S$. But if $U$ belongs to $S$ it will be called the MAXIMUM of $S$.

From condition 1 in the definition just given we see that if $S$ has a least upper bound $U$, then $S$ is contained in the half-line $(-\infty, U]$, so $S$ is bounded above.

EXAMPLES. In the set $S = \{-1, -1/2, -1/3, -1/4, \ldots -1/n, \ldots, 0\}$, $0$ is the maximum, hence the least upper bound.

In the set $S = \{1, 3/2, 5/3, 7/4, 9/5, \ldots, 2 - 1/n, \ldots\}$, 2 is the least upper bound, but not the maximum.

In these two examples, the least upper bound is an accumulation point for $S$. In the finite set $S = \{0, 1, 2, 3, 4\}$ the maximum 4 is not an accumulation point.

In the set $S$, union of the half-line $(-\infty, 0)$ and the point 1, the maximum is 1, which is not an accumulation point.

An analogous definition is given for the GREATEST LOWER BOUND or INFIMUM of $S$, which we call the MINIMUM of $S$, when it belongs to $S$.

We shall not undertake here the task of formulating these definitions and providing examples, but we suggest that this be done as an exercise. As a further exercise, try to prove the following proposition.

PROPOSITION. *If a set $S$ of real numbers has a least upper bound $U$, then $U$ is the only least upper bound of $S$ (similarly for the greatest lower bound $L$ of $S$); moreover, $L \leq U$.*

We denote $U = \sup S$, $L = \inf S$.

We now deal with the much more important question: is it true that every set $S$, which is bounded above (respectively bounded below) has a least upper bound (respectively a greatest lower bound)?

THEOREM. *Every nonempty set $S$ of real numbers which is bounded above has a least upper bound. Similarly, every nonempty set which is bounded below has a greatest lower bound.*

*Proof.* If the set $S$ has no limit superior, since it is bounded, it must be finite (see the remark following the Bolzano and Weierstrass theorem on page 37). Thus, the largest of its members is the maximum and, therefore, the least upper bound of $S$.

If, however, the set $S$ has limit superior $\alpha$, then either $\alpha$ is the least upper bound of $S$, or there exists some element $x_0$ in $S$ such that $x_0 > \alpha$; at any rate, given an integer $N > 0$, so large that $\alpha + 1/N < x_0$, the comment on page 37 implies that there exists only a finite number of elements in $S$, $x_0, x_1, \ldots, x_n$, larger than $\alpha + 1/N$; in this case, the largest of the numbers $x_0, x_1, \ldots, x_n$ is the maximum, consequently the least upper bound of $S$.

COROLLARY. *If the set $S$ is bounded above and has a limit superior $\alpha$, then $\alpha \leq U = \sup S$.*

*Similarly, if the set $S$ is bounded below and has a limit inferior $\beta$, then $\beta \geq L = \inf S$.*

This corollary follows from the proof of the theorem.

**Exercises**

*1.* Determine which of the following sets of real numbers are bounded above, bounded below, or bounded; also determine their greatest lower bound and least upper bound.

(a) The set of all even integers.
(b) The set of all strictly negative integers.
(c) The set $\{0, 1, 2, 3, 19, -5\}$.
(d) The set $\{3/2, -4/3, 5/4, -6/5, 7/6, -8/7, \ldots\}$.
(e) The set of all rational numbers whose denominator is of type $2^n$ ($n \geqslant 0$, integer) and whose numerator is an integer in $[4, 8)$.

2. Determine the accumulation points of the following sets of real numbers.

(a) The set of all rational numbers between 0 and 1.
(b) The set $\{1, -1, 2, -2, 3, -3, \ldots, n, -n, \ldots\}$.
(c) The set of all rational numbers $m/2^n$, where $m$, $n$ are integers, $m, n \geqslant 0$.
(d) The set $\{1, 2, 3\}$.
(e) The set of all numbers of type $1/m + 1/n$, where $m$, $n > 0$ are integers.

3. Show that if $S'$ is the set of all the accumulation points of the set $S$, and if $S''$ is the set of all the accumulation points of the set $S'$, then $S''$ is contained in $S'$.

4. Determine the limit superior and limit inferior of the following sets of real numbers.

(a) $\{2, -2, 1/2, -1/2, 2/3, -2/3, \ldots, n/(n + 1), -n/(n + 1), \ldots\}$.
(b) $\{0, 1, 2, 3, \ldots, n, \ldots\}$.
(c) $\{1, -1, 1/2, -1/2, 1/3, -1/3, \ldots, 1/n, -1/n, \ldots\}$
(d) $\{2, \sqrt{2}, \sqrt[2]{2}, \ldots, \sqrt[n]{2}, \ldots\}$

(e) The set of all real numbers $\dfrac{1}{m^2} + \dfrac{1}{n^2}$, where $m$, $n = 1, 2, \ldots$

(f) The set of all real numbers $\dfrac{(-1)^n}{n} + \dfrac{n}{2n + 1}$, where $n = 1, 2, \ldots$

5. Determine the greatest lower bound and the least upper bound of the sets in the preceding exercise.

6. Prove that if a nonempty set $S$ of real numbers has a least upper bound $U$, then $U$ is the only least upper bound of $S$; similarly for the greatest lower bound $L$; moreover, $L \leqslant U$.

7. Let $S$, $S'$ be two nonempty bounded sets of real numbers; let $T$ be the set of all real numbers which are sums $s + s'$, with $s \in S$, $s' \in S'$. Show that $T$ is also bounded and

$$\sup T = \sup S + \sup S',$$
$$\inf T = \inf S + \inf S'.$$

8. A set $S$ of real numbers is called *dense* when every real number is an accumulation point for the set $S$. Prove the following.

(a) The set of all irrational numbers is dense.

(b) The set of all numbers of type $m/2^n$, where $m$, $n$ are integers, is dense.

9.* Verify that the construction below provides an example of a set $S$ of real numbers with the following property: denoting $S_1 = S$ and $S_n$ being the set of all accumulation points of $S_{n-1}$, then the sets $S_1$, $S_2$, . . ., $S_n$, . . . are all distinct.

The construction of $S$ is done as follows: we let $A_1$ be the set of all real numbers $1/2^m$ with $m = 1, 2, 3, \ldots$, $A_2$ be the set of all real numbers

$$1 + \frac{1}{2^m} + \frac{1}{2^{m+n}}$$

with $m$, $n = 1, 2, 3, \ldots$, and, generally, $A_r$ be the set of all real numbers

$$(r - 1) + \frac{1}{2^m} + \frac{1}{2^{m+n}} + \cdots + \frac{1}{2^{m+n+\ldots+q}}$$

with $m$, $n$, . . ., $q = 1, 2, 3, \ldots$

Then, the set $S$, union of the sets $A_1$, $A_2$, . . ., $A_r$, . . ., has the above-mentioned property.

* Cf. H. G. EGGLESTON'S *Elementary Real Analysis*, The University Press, Cambridge, 1962.

# 5

# Sequences of Real Numbers

As we have seen in Chapter 1, every correspondence of the set of natural numbers into the set of real numbers, defines a real SEQUENCE. Denoting by $a_n$ the image of the natural number $n$ by this correspondence, then $a_1, a_2, \ldots, a_n, \ldots$ are the TERMS of the sequence.

EXAMPLE 1. The correspondence that associates to every natural number its inverse, defines a sequence, whose terms are $1, 1/2, 1/3, 1/4, \ldots,$ $1/n, \ldots.$.

In this example there is a *simple rule* that tells which are the terms of sequence; it consists in taking for $a_n$ the inverse of the index $n$; as this same rule may be applied to every integer $n \geq 1$, we say that $1/n$ is the GENERAL TERM of the sequence.

Thus, to say that an expression, where the integer $n$ appears, is the general term of a sequence, means that, by replacing in this expression, successively, $n$ by $1, 2, 3, \ldots,$ we obtain all the terms of the sequence.

Let us point out that, given a sequence, it is not always possible to determine its general terms as a simple * expression in which there appears the integer $n$. We illustrate this by Example 2.

EXAMPLE 2. Let us consider the rule that associates to every integer $n \geq 1$ the number $a_n$ of natural numbers smaller than $n$ and prime with $n$. This rule defines a sequence, whose first terms we shall write explicitly, as shown in Table 1.

There is no simple expression, by means of the number $n$, which allows us to compute $a_n$. This correspondence is known as the EULER *indicator of the number $n$.*

---

* The term *simple expression* does not have mathematical rigor, and depends, of course, on the reader's knowledge. Here, it will mean any expression using only the more current operations and functions.

Table 1

| $n$ | $a_n$ | Because the following integers are smaller than $n$ and prime with $n$ |
|---|---|---|
| 1 | 0 | — |
| 2 | 1 | 1 |
| 3 | 2 | 1, 2 |
| 4 | 2 | 1, 3 |
| 5 | 4 | 1, 2, 3, 4 |
| 6 | 2 | 1, 5 |
| 7 | 6 | 1, 2, 3, 4, 5, 6 |
| 8 | 4 | 1, 3, 5, 7 |

EXAMPLE 3. Let us consider the rule that associates to each integer $n \geq 1$ the number $\sqrt[n]{2}$. It defines a sequence of real numbers whose general terms are $a_n = \sqrt[n]{2}$.

In what follows we shall cite many more examples of sequences.

In the previous introduction of the real numbers (Chapter 3), we made use of sequences of rational numbers, as well as of notions that are essentially related to the concept of limit. Nevertheless, in that discussion, it was not feasible to elaborate on these points. Now, we shall study, in more detail, the sequences of real numbers, establishing general theorems.

We shall frequently use two phrases, whose meaning we now explain.

*A Property P on the Terms of a Sequence $(a_n)$*
*is valid for every sufficiently large n*

This means that it is possible to find an integer $n_0$ (for example, $n_0 = 10$, or 128, or 1325, etc.) such that *every term $a_n$, with $n \geq n_0$*, satisfies the property *P*.

*A Property P on the Terms of a Sequence $(a_n)$*
*is valid for arbitrarily large Values of n*

This means that for every given index $n_0$ (for example, $n_0 = 16$, or 227, or 31245, etc.) *there exists some index $n \geq n_0$* such that the term $a_n$ satisfies the property *P*.

Obviously, if a property *P* is valid for every sufficiently large integer *n*, it is also valid for arbitrarily large values of *n*. The converse is not true.

EXAMPLE 1. Consider the sequence having the general term $a_n = 1/n$ and the following property *P*: the term $a_n$ has the property *P* when $0 < a_n < 3/25$. We see that $a_9 = 1/9 < 3/25$, while $a_8 = 1/8 > 3/25$; since the terms of the sequence $(a_n)$ are decreasing, the property *P* is satisfied for every index $n \geq n_0 = 9$.

EXAMPLE 2. Consider the sequence having the general term $a_n = (-1)^n n/(n+1)$; its first terms are $a_1 = -1/2$, $a_2 = 2/3$, $a_3 = -3/4$, $a_4 = 4/5$, $a_5 = -5/6$, etc. Consider the property $P$: the term $a_n$ has the property $P$ when $23/24 < a_n < 1$. Since $a_{23} = -23/24$, $a_{24} = 24/25$, and since the terms with even index are all positive, increasing in value, and always less than 1, it follows that, given any index $n_0$ (for example, $n_0 = 31$), then $a_{32} = 32/33$ satisfies the property $P$; thus $P$ is valid for some index $n \geq n_0$. However, the property $P$ is *not satisfied* for every sufficiently large integer $n$, since it is false when $n$ is an odd integer (because, then, $a_n < 0$).

We turn now to one of the fundamental notions in mathematics—the notion of LIMIT. First we shall study it in the case of sequences.

Before giving a definition, we shall examine intuitive examples. Consider the sequence whose general term is $a_n = 1/n$. Marking its first terms in a straight line (with a fixed origin, a given orientation, and a given unit of length), we see intuitively that the terms of the sequence accumulate in the neighborhood of 0; actually, we have already introduced the notion of accumulation point to describe such a situation. But in this particular example, it is not only true that there exist *infinitely* many terms of the sequence $(a_n)$ contained in each interval of the type $(a, b)$, with $a < 0 < b$; even better, each one of the intervals $(a, b)$ contains *all* the terms of sequence, from a convenient index on.

Thus, for each interval $(a, b)$, with $a < 0 < b$, consider the property $P$: the term $a_n$ has the property $P$ when $a_n$ is in $(a, b)$. In this example, $P$ is satisfied for every sufficiently large $n$. Since this is true for *every* interval $(a, b)$, with $a < 0 < b$, it means that after disregarding a convenient number of initial terms of the sequence, all the other terms of $(a_n)$ will be contained "in the neighborhood" of 0. That is why we say that 0 is *the* LIMIT *of the sequence* $(a_n)$, and we write $\lim 1/n = 0$.

Now we give a general definition of the concept of limit.

DEFINITION. *The real number $s$ is called the limit of the sequence $(a_n)$ of real numbers when for every given natural number $N$ (as large as we like) there exists an index $n_0$ (which depends on $N$) such that, for every $n \geq n_0$ we have $|a_n - s| < 1/N$, that is, $s - 1/N < a_n < s + 1/N$. If a sequence $(a_n)$ has limit $s$, we say that it is* CONVERGENT *to $s$.*

By introducing a new auxiliary terminology, we rephrase the definition of limit in a more suggestive form. This is achieved by defining the terms NEIGHBORHOOD OF A REAL NUMBER, LIMIT AT INFINITY, and NEIGHBORHOOD AT INFINITY.

We call a *neighborhood of the real number $s$* each interval of the form $[s - 1/N, s + 1/N]$ or $(s - 1/N, s + 1/N)$, where $N$ is any natural integer; the first intervals are more precisely called CLOSED neighborhoods, while the last ones are the OPEN neighborhoods.

The concept of limit of a sequence (as well as that of accumulation point) concerns exclusively the *terms with sufficiently large index*. Thus, we may say that the notion of limit is defined when *n increases indefinitely* or, in other words, when *n approaches or tends to infinity*. Since there is here no possibility of confusion, we use the symbol $\infty$ to indicate "plus infinity," and write $\lim\limits_{n\to\infty} a_n = s$ to stress that *s* is the limit of the sequence $(a_n)$, as *n* tends to $\infty$. This is just another notation for $\lim a_n = s$.

Now we comment on *neighborhood of infinity*.

DEFINITION. *A neighborhood $U_n$ of infinity, (in the set of natural integers\*) is the set of all natural integers $m > n$.*

Thus, each integer $n \geqslant 0$ gives rise to a neighborhood $U_n$ of infinity. The larger *n* is, the "smaller" the neighborhood $U_n$ will be, in the following sense: if $m > n$, then the set $U_m$ is a part of $U_n$ (distinct from $U_n$).

EXAMPLE. The set of all the integers larger than 3, or 100, or 1827, etc., are neighborhoods of infinity. However, the set of all multiples of 3 larger than 325 is not a neighborhood of infinity.

With this terminology, we rephrase the definition of limit.

DEFINITION. *The real number s is the limit of the sequence $(a_n)$ when, for every neighborhood $U_N$ of s, there exists a neighborhood $U_{n_0}$ of infinity, such that if n is in $U_{n_0}$, then $a_n$ is in $U_N$.*

Therefore, each neighborhood of *s* contains all the terms of the sequence with a finite number of exceptions.

This definition has the advantage of being similar to the one that we shall give later for the limit of a function at a point.

EXAMPLE 1. The sequence 1, 1, 1, ..., 1, ... has limit equal to 1.

EXAMPLE 2. The sequence $a_1 = 1$, $a_2 = 1/2$, $a_3 = 1/2^2$, ..., $a_n = 1/2^{n-1}$, ... has limit equal to 0. Indeed, given any positive integer $N$, for instance, $N = 10, 100, 1000, 10000, \ldots$, we may find an integer $n_0$ with the properties indicated in the definition. As an illustration:

if $N = \quad 10$ then $n_0 = \quad 5$: if $n \geq \quad 5$ then $a_n \leq 1/2^4 < 1/10$;

if $N = \quad 100$ then $n_0 = \quad 8$: if $n \geq \quad 8$ then $a_n \leq 1/2^7 < 1/100$;

if $N = \quad 1000$ then $n_0 = 11$: if $n \geq 11$ then $a_n \leq 1/2^{10} < 1/1000$;

if $N = 10000$ then $n_0 = 15$: if $n \geq 15$ then $a_n \leq 1/2^{14} < 1/10000$; etc.

EXAMPLE 3. The sequence 1, $-1$, 1, $-1$, 1, $-1$, ... does not have any limit.

---

\* Later we shall also define a neighborhood of infinity, in the set of *real numbers*.

EXAMPLE 4. The sequence 2, 3, 5, 5, 5, 5, ... has limit equal to 5.

EXAMPLE 5. The sequence $1/2$, $-1/2$, $2/3$, $-2/3$, $3/4$, $-3/4$, $4/5$, $-4/5$, ... does not have any limit. Precisely, the subsequence of terms with odd index, $1/2$, $2/3$, $3/4$, $4/5$, ..., has limit equal to 1; similarly, the subsequence of terms with even index, $-1/2$, $-2/3$, $-3/4$, $-4/5$, ... has limit equal to $-1$. Since these limits of the subsequences are *distinct*, considering the neighborhood $(1/2, 3/2)$ of 1 and $(-3/2, -1/2)$ of $-1$, we see that each one fails to contain infinitely many terms of the sequence (which are contained in the other one); thus, neither 1, nor $-1$ may be a limit of the given sequence.

We now state lemmas and propositions concerning the notion of limit of a sequence.

LEMMA. *Let* $(a_n)$ *be a sequence of real numbers. If there exists a real number* $k > 0$, *and for each given natural number* $N$, *there exists an index* $n_0$ *such that* $|a_n - s| < k/N$, *for every index* $n \geq n_0$, *then* $\lim a_n = s$.

Indeed, to show that $\lim a_n = s$, let $M$ be any given integer (as large as we like). Taking an integer $N \geq kM$, we have $k/N \leq 1/M$. By hypothesis, given $N$, there exists $n_0$ such that if $n \geq n_0$ then $|a_n - s| \leq k/N \leq 1/M$. Thus, the condition for $s$ to be limit of the sequence $(a_n)$ is verified.

UNIQUENESS OF THE LIMIT. *If a sequence* $(a_n)$ *is convergent, then it has only one limit.*

Indeed, let us assume that $s$, $s'$ are two different limits for the convergent sequence $(a_n)$; for example, $s < s'$. Let $N$ be chosen so large that $1/N < (s' - s)/2$. Thus $s + 1/N < s' - 1/N$. By the definition of limit, there exists an index $n_0$ such that $s - 1/N < a_n < s + 1/N$ provided $n \geq n_0$; similarly, there exists an index $n_1$ such that $s' - 1/N < a_n < s' + 1/N$ provided $n \geq n_1$. Considering the indices $n$ larger than both $n_0$, $n_1$, we must have, at the same time, $s - 1/N < a_n < s + 1/N < s' - 1/N < a_n < s' + 1/N$, which is impossible. Hence $s = s'$.

PROPOSITION. *Let* $(a_n)$ *be a convergent sequence. Then, the set composed of the real numbers* $a_1$, $a_2$, $a_3$, ... *is a bounded set of real numbers.*

In fact, let $s$ be the limit of the sequence $(a_n)$. Given, for example, the integer $N = 1$, there exists an index $n_0$ such that $s - 1 < a_n < s + 1$, provided that $n \geq n_0$. This tells us that all the terms of the sequence, distinct from the initial terms $a_1$, $a_2$, ..., $a_{n_0} - 1$ lie in the interval $(s - 1, s + 1)$. Denoting by $b_1$, $b_2$, respectively, the smallest and largest of the initial terms $a_1$, $a_2$, ..., $a_{n_0-1}$, we see that all the terms of $(a_n)$ are in the set obtained as union of the intervals $[b_1, b_2]$ and $(s - 1, s + 1)$, at any rate, in a bounded set (cf. page 33).

As we have seen in Example 3, page 44, it is possible that a sequence has no limit even though the set of its terms is bounded.

This possibility stresses again the importance of distinguishing carefully between a sequence and the set of its terms.

COROLLARY. *If* $(a_n)$ *is a sequence of real numbers such that the set of terms* $a_1$, $a_2$, $a_3$, ..., $a_n$, ... *is not bounded, then* $(a_n)$ *cannot be a convergent sequence.*

Thus, the sequence 1, 2, 3, 4, 5, ... cannot be convergent.

If a sequence $(a_n)$ is not convergent, it is called DIVERGENT. Therefore, the unbounded sequences constitute the first example of divergent sequences. Later, we shall study the types of divergent sequences.

PROPOSITION. *Every subsequence of a convergent sequence is convergent to the same limit.*

In fact, let $(a_n)$ be a sequence converging to the limit $s$. Let $a_{n_1}$, $a_{n_2}$, $a_{n_3}$, ... be a subsequence, extracted from the given sequence (for example, the subsequence of all the terms having index multiple of 3, or having index terminating by the digit 7, etc.; the subsequence may be arbitrarily chosen). We shall show that the subsequence $(a_{n_m})$ has limit equal to $s$. For this purpose, let $N$ be any natural number (as large as we like); then, there exists an index $n_0$ such that $|a_n - s| < 1/N$, provided $n \geqslant n_0$. Let $m_0$ be the smallest integer such that the index $n_{m_0}$, in the given subsequence, be larger than $n_0$: $n_{m_0} \geqslant n_0$. Then, if $n \geqslant n_{m_0}$, we have also $|a_n - s| < 1/N$. In particular, considering only those indices $n_m$ corresponding to the given subsequence, we have $|a_{n_m} - s| < 1/N$, provided $n_m \geqslant n_{m_0}$; that is, provided $m \geqslant m_0$. This means that the subsequence $(a_{n_m})$ converges to $s$ (since $N$ was arbitrary).

## Monotone Increasing and Decreasing Sequences

A sequence $(a_n)$ of real numbers is called a MONOTONE *sequence* whenever either $a_1 \leqslant a_2 \leqslant a_3 \leqslant ... \leqslant a_n \leqslant ...$ or $a_1 \geqslant a_2 \geqslant a_3 \geqslant ... \geqslant a_n \geqslant ...$.

In the first case, we say that it is a MONOTONE INCREASING *sequence*, while in the second case, it is a MONOTONE DECREASING *sequence*.

If we have $a_1 < a_2 < a_3 < ... < a_n < ...$, the sequence is said to be STRICTLY INCREASING; similarly, if $a_1 > a_2 > a_3 > ... > a_n > ...$, it is called STRICTLY DECREASING.

EXAMPLES. The sequence 1, 2, 3, ..., $n$, ... is a monotone strictly increasing sequence.

The sequence 1, 1/2, 1/3, ..., 1/n, ... is a monotone strictly decreasing sequence.

The sequence 1, 1, 2, 2, 3, 3, . . ., $n$, $n$, . . . is a monotone increasing sequence.

The sequence 1, 1, 1, 1, . . . is both a monotone increasing and a monotone decreasing sequence.

The sequence $1/2$, $-1/2$, $1/3$, $-1/3$, . . ., $1/n$, $-1/n$, . . . is not a monotone sequence.

In a monotone sequence, it may happen that the set of its terms is a bounded set of real numbers (as in the second, fourth, and fifth sequences, above). In the following proposition we consider such monotone sequences.

PROPOSITION. *Convergence of Bounded Monotone Sequences. If $(a_n)$ is a monotone sequence which is bounded, then $(a_n)$ is convergent. Precisely, if $(a_n)$ is decreasing then $\lim a_n = \inf a_n$; if $(a_n)$ is increasing, then $\lim a_n = \sup a_n$.*

Assume, for example, that $(a_n)$ is a monotone increasing sequence whose set of terms is bounded. Let us show that $(a_n)$ is convergent and $\lim a_n = \sup a_n$.

Since the set of terms is bounded, it has a least upper bound $U = \sup a_n$. Given any positive integer $N$, by the definition of least upper bound, there exists a term $a_{n_0}$ such that $U - 1/N < a_{n_0}$; since the sequence $(a_n)$ is monotone increasing, then $U - 1/N < a_{n_0} \leqslant a_n < U < U + 1/N$ for every index $n \geqslant n_0$. Hence, $U = \lim a_n$.

The proof is similar for the case of monotone decreasing sequences.

## *Application of BOLZANO and WEIERSTRASS Theorem:*

PROPOSITION. *Any bounded sequence $(x_n)$ contains a monotone subsequence, which is therefore convergent.*

If the set of terms $x_1$, $x_2$, . . ., $x_n$, . . . is finite, there are infinitely many indices $n_1 < n_2 < \ldots, < n_m < \ldots$ such that $x_{n_1} = x_{n_2} = \ldots = x_{n_m} = \ldots$; this is a monotonically increasing (and decreasing) subsequence of $(x_n)$, clearly convergent.

If, however, there are infinitely many distinct terms in the sequence $(x_n)$, since the set $S$ of terms of $(x_n)$ is bounded by hypothesis, there exists an accumulation point $s$ for the set $S$, as follows from the Bolzano and Weierstrass theorem.

Thus, given any integer $N_1 > 0$, there exist infinitely many distinct terms of the sequence $(x_n)$ such that $0 < |x_n - s| < 1/N_1$; let $n_1$ be the smallest index for which $0 < |x_{n_1} - s| < 1/N_1$.

Taking $N_2$ such that $1/N_2 < |x_{n_1} - s|$, by the same token there exist again infinitely many distinct terms of the sequence $(x_n)$ such that $0 < |x_n - s| < 1/N_2$; let $n_2$ be the smallest index such that $n_1 < n_2$ and $0 < |x_{n_2} - s| < 1/N_2$.

Repeating the same argument, we obtain a subsequence $x_{n_1}, x_{n_2}, \ldots,$ $x_{n_m}, \ldots$ of the given sequence, all of whose terms are distinct, and have $s$ as an accumulation point; moreover, $|x_{n_1} - s| > |x_{n_2} - s| > \ldots >$ $|x_{n_m} - s| > \ldots$.

Now, infinitely many of the terms $x_{n_1}, x_{n_2}, \ldots$ are either smaller than $s$, or else infinitely many of these terms are greater than $s$. In the first case, those terms smaller than $s$ form a subsequence of the given sequence which is monotonically increasing; in the other case we obtain a monotonically decreasing subsequence. In each instance, $s$ is the limit of the sequence, since the absolute value $|s - x_{n_m}|$ may be chosen arbitrarily small (provided $m$ is large enough).

COROLLARY. *If $S$ is an infinite bounded set of real numbers, there exist distinct numbers $x_1, x_2, \ldots, x_n, \ldots$ in $S$ such that the sequence $(x_n)$ is monotone and, therefore, convergent.*

Since $S$ is an infinite set, if we start writing its elements, one after the other (for example, as $x_1, x_2, \ldots, x_n$), at every step there exists still another element in the set $S$. In other words, there exists a one-to-one correspondence from the set of all the natural integers into the set $S$ (maybe onto the whole set $S$, or maybe only onto a part of $S$, smaller than $S$).*

Therefore, $S$ contains a part whose elements $x_1, x_2, \ldots, x_n, \ldots$ may be considered as the terms of a sequence. Since $S$ is bounded, so is the sequence $(x_n)$; by the proposition, it contains a monotone subsequence, which is therefore convergent.

### Classification of Divergent Sequences

It is now possible to give a classification of divergent sequences. Let $(a_n)$ be a divergent sequence.

If $(a_n)$ is monotone, its terms either *increase* in value beyond any bound, or *decrease* beyond any bound; otherwise $(a_n)$ would be contained in some interval and, therefore, it would be a convergent sequence by a previous proposition.

If $(a_n)$ is not monotone, let us consider the set of real numbers composed of its terms $a_n$.

### Case 1.    *The Set of Terms $a_n$ is Bounded*

Either the set of terms $a_n$ is $(a)$ a finite set, or $(b)$ an infinite set.

In the first instance $(a)$ above, as the sequence $(a_n)$ is divergent, it is impossible that all the terms with sufficiently large index coincide; there-

---

* See Appendix B for a more detailed discussion of infinite sets.

fore, whatever be the index $n_0$, not all terms of the sequence with index larger than $n_0$ are equal.

EXAMPLE. 1, 2, 1, 2, 1, 2, 1, 2, . . .

In the second instance $(b)$ above, using the Bolzano and Weierstrass theorem, we deduce the existence of at least one accumulation point for the set of terms $a_n$. Since the sequence $(a_n)$ is divergent, this accumulation point cannot be the *only* one (as we should verify); thus, the set of terms $a_n$ has at least two distinct accumulation points.

EXAMPLE. $1/2$, $-2/3$, $3/4$, $-4/5$, $5/6$, $-6/7$, . . ..

Then, $1$, $-1$ are the accumulation points of the set of terms.

In this case, we say that $(a_n)$ is an OSCILLATING sequence with finite accumulation points.

### Case 2. *The Set of Terms $a_n$ is Unbounded*

This set contains real numbers of arbitrarily large absolute value; they may be positive as well as negative.

Several possibilities may arise, as shown by these examples:

$1, 1, 1/2, 2, 1/3, 3, \ldots, 1/n, n, \ldots$
(this is a sequence with infinite oscillation, having a subsequence with accumulation point equal to 0)

$1, -1, 2, -2, 3, -3, \ldots, n, -n, \ldots$
(this is a sequence with infinite oscillation, and having no convergent subsequence)

$1, 0, 2, 1, 3, 2, \ldots, n, n - 1, \ldots$
(this is a sequence which we might convention to call CONVERGENT TO PLUS INFINITY)

Summarizing:

Divergent sequences
- Monotone
  - Increasing beyond any bound
  - Decreasing beyond any bound
- Not monotone
  - Finite oscillation
  - Infinite oscillation
  - Convergent to $+\infty$, or $-\infty$

### Operations with Sequences

Let $(a_n)$, $(b_n)$ be two sequences of real numbers, converging respectively to the limits $s$, $t$; that is, $s = \lim a_n$, $t = \lim b_n$. Then we have:

(1) The sequence $(a_n + b_n)$ is convergent, and $\lim (a_n + b_n) = s + t$.
(2) The sequence $(a_n - b_n)$ is convergent, and $\lim (a_n - b_n) = s - t$.
(3) The sequence $(a_n b_n)$ is convergent, and $\lim (a_n b_n) = st$.
(4) If $t \neq 0$, the sequence* $a_n/b_n$ is convergent, and $\lim a_n/b_n = s/t$.

*Proof.* (1) We need to show that $s + t$ may be arbitrarily approached by the elements $a_n + b_n$ for every sufficiently large index. The only information we have is that the differences $|s - a_n|$, $|t - b_n|$ are less than $1/N$, provided $n$ is large enough.

Our aim is to express the difference $|(s + t) - (a_n + b_n)|$ in terms of $|s - a_n|$, $|t - b_n|$. This is easily done, using the triangle inequality

$$|(s + t) - (a_n + b_n)| = |(s - a_n) + (t - b_n)| \leqslant |s - a_n| + |t - b_n|$$
$$< \frac{1}{N} + \frac{1}{N} = \frac{2}{N}.$$

Since $N$ is arbitrary and the above inequality hold for all sufficiently large $n$, by the lemma on page 45, it follows that $\lim (a_n + b_n) = s + t$.

(2) The proof is similar.

(3) For the multiplication the following equality is the crucial part of the proof.

$$st - a_n b_n = (s - a_n)t + s(t - b_n) - (s - a_n)(t - b_n).$$

It expresses the difference $st - a_n b_n$, to be made small, in terms of the differences $s - a_n$, $t - b_n$, which are small in absolute value for every large enough index $n$.

Explicitly, given any positive integer $N$, we have

$$|s - a_n| < \frac{1}{N}, \quad |t - b_n| < \frac{1}{N}$$

for every sufficiently large index $n$. Hence, for large values of $n$, we have

$$|st - a_n b_n| \leqslant |s - a_n| \cdot |t| + |s| \cdot |t - b_n| + |s - a_n| \cdot |t - b_n|$$
$$< \frac{1}{N} |t| + \frac{1}{N} |s| + \frac{1}{N} \cdot \frac{1}{N} \leqslant \frac{1}{N} (|t| + |s| + 1).$$

---

* We must disregard all the terms $b_n = 0$; however, since $\lim b_n = t \neq 0$, it is certain that $b_n \neq 0$ for every sufficiently large index $n$.

Since $|t| + |s| + 1$ is a fixed number, which is independent of $N$, the same lemma already quoted implies that $\lim (a_n b_n) = st$.

(4) By part (3), it is sufficient to prove that $\lim 1/b_n = 1/t$. This implies that $\lim a_n/b_n = \lim a_n$, $\lim 1/b_n = s/t$.

Given any integer $N > 0$, as large as we like (for example, such that $1/N < |t|/2$, there exists an index $n_0$ such that $|t - b_n| < 1/N$, whenever $n \geqslant n_0$. Since $1/N < |t|/2$, we must have $|b_n| > |t|/2$ when $n \geqslant n_0$; otherwise, $|b_n| \leqslant |t|/2$ and also $|t - b_n| < 1/N$, hence $|t| = |b_n + (t - b_n)| \leqslant |b_n| + |t - b_n| \leqslant |t|/2 + 1/N < |t|/2 + |t|/2 = |t|$, which is a contradiction.

Now, for $n \geqslant n_0$ we have

$$\left| \frac{1}{b_n} - \frac{1}{t} \right| = \frac{|t - b_n|}{|b_n| \cdot |t|} < \frac{1}{|t|} \cdot \frac{2}{|t|} \cdot \frac{1}{N} < \frac{2}{|t|^2} \cdot \frac{1}{N},$$

hence $\lim 1/b_n = 1/t$.


## Inequalities with Sequences

*Let $(a_n)$, $(b_n)$ be two convergent sequences of real numbers, and let $s$, $t$ be their limits. If $a_n \leqslant b_n$ for every sufficiently large index $n$, then $s = \lim a_n \leqslant \lim b_n = t$.*

It is sufficient to prove that *if $(c_n)$ is a convergent sequence such that all its terms with sufficiently large index are nonnegative, $c_n \geqslant 0$, then $u = \lim c_n \geqslant 0$.*

In fact, if this has been proved, let $c_n = b_n - a_n$; thus $c_n \geqslant 0$ for every sufficiently large $n$; hence, $\lim c_n = \lim b_n - \lim a_n \geqslant 0$; that is, $\lim a_n \leqslant \lim b_n$.

Thus, we must prove the above assertion. Given any integer $N > 0$, there exists an index $n_0$ such that if $n \geqslant n_0$ then $|u - c_n| < 1/N$. If we had $u < 0$, then taking $N$ so large that $u + 1/N < 0$, it would follow that $u - 1/N < c_n < u + 1/N < 0$, which is impossible, since $c_n \geqslant 0$ for every sufficiently large index $n$. Thus, $u \geqslant 0$.

*Note.* From this proposition, it follows that if $(a_n)$, $(b_n)$ are convergent sequences, and $a_n < b_n$ for every sufficiently large index $n$, then $\lim a_n \leqslant \lim b_n$. We cannot conclude, however, under the same hypothesis, that $\lim a_n < \lim b_n$.

In particular, if the convergent sequence $(a_n)$ satisfies $a_n < b$ (or $a_n > b$) for every sufficiently large $n$, it follows only that $\lim a_n \leqslant b$ (or $\lim a_n \geqslant b$), but not, in general, that $\lim a_n < b$ (or $\lim a_n > b$).

EXAMPLE. The convergent sequence $1, 1/2, 1/3, \ldots, 1/n, \ldots$ has limit $0$, even though all its terms are strictly positive.

## CAUCHY Convergence Criterion

We now suggest a careful examination of the definition of a sequence of real numbers. Since we have defined the concept of limit in order to know whether a sequence $(a_n)$ has a limit, we must (at least in principle) *try* every real number to see whether it satisfies the condition in the definition. For example, given the sequence $(a_n)$, we take the number 1 (or 3, or 5, or $n$, etc. . . . .) and check whether given *any* integer $N > 0$, it is possible to find an integer $n_0$ such that if $n > n_0$ then $|a_n - 1| < 1/N$. If we find a number $s$ satisfying the condition above, then we say that $(a_n)$ converges to $s$; and, by theory already developed, we know that $s$ will be the *only* limit of the sequence $(a_n)$; also, in every neighborhood of $s$ (no matter how small it may be), we may find all the terms of the sequence except, at most, a finite number among them. This means, intuitively, that the terms of the sequence concentrate ultimately in a "vicinity" of each other.

The great disadvantage in this definition, as it stands, is that to find whether a sequence has a limit, we must, beforehand, have an idea of the possible candidates for this limit (if any such exist); otherwise, there will be infinitely many numbers to try, and this cannot be carried out in practice.

Therefore, we need a method that will enable us *to decide whether a sequence is convergent without guessing which will be its possible limit.* It should be based only on the notion of vicinity of terms of the sequence.

This is precisely the content of the so-called *Cauchy convergence criterion.*

We first define a FUNDAMENTAL or *Cauchy sequence* of real numbers; immediately we recall that in Chapter 3 we defined a fundamental or Cauchy sequence of *rational* numbers; consequently our present definition is an extension of the preceding one.

Let $(a_n)$ be a sequence of real numbers. We say that *it is a fundamental or Cauchy sequence whenever, given any natural number $N$, there exists an index $n_0$ such that if $m$, $n \geq n_0$ then $|a_m - a_n| < 1/N$.* This means that, disregarding a finite number of initial terms, the terms of the sequence concentrate in intervals of arbitrarily small length.

Therefore, *the set of terms of any fundamental sequence $(a_n)$ is bounded.*

For, as we have said, given any natural number $N$ (and even $N = 1$ is enough for our argument), there exists an index $n_0$ such that if $m$, $n \geq n_0$ then $|a_n - a_m| < 1$. In particular, with $m = n_0$, we have $|a_n - a_{n_0}| < 1$; that is, $a_{n_0} - 1 \leq a_n \leq a_{n_0} + 1$, for every index $n \geq n_0$.

For the finite number of initial terms $a_1, a_2, \ldots, a_{n_0-1}$ of the sequence, we do not need to worry; taking a natural number $M$ so large that

$$|a_1| < M, \quad |a_2| < M, \quad \ldots |a_{n_0} - 1| < M, \quad |a_{n_0} + 1| < M,$$

then the set of terms of the sequence $(a_n)$ is contained in the interval $(-M, M)$, so it is bounded.

PROPOSITION. *Every convergent sequence of real numbers is a fundamental sequence.*

In fact, let $\lim\limits_{n \to \infty} a_n = s$: thus, given any integer $n > 0$, we have $|a_n - s| < 1/N$, provided $n \geqslant n_0$ (conveniently chosen index). In particular, if $m, n \geqslant n_0$, we have

$$|a_m - a_n| = |(a_m - s) + (s - a_n)| \leqslant |a_m - s| + |s - a_n| < 2/N.$$

Since $N$ is arbitrary, we conclude that $(a_n)$ is a fundamental sequence. Now, the following important question arises.

If $(a_n)$ is a fundamental sequence of *real numbers*, is it true that $(a_n)$ is convergent?

THEOREM OF CAUCHY (GENERAL CONVERGENCE CRITERION). *The sequence $(a_n)$ of real numbers is convergent if and only if it is a fundamental sequence.*

*Proof.* The preceding proposition tells us that every convergent sequence of real numbers is a fundamental sequence.

Conversely, let $(a_n)$ be a fundamental sequence of real numbers and let us show that $(a_n)$ is convergent. Since the set of terms of this sequence is bounded (by the proposition on page 47), there exists a convergent subsequence $(a_{n_m})$, whose limit we denote by $s = \lim\limits_{m \to \infty} a_{n_m}$.

We now prove that the given sequence $(a_n)$ converges also to $s$.

Since $(a_n)$ is a fundamental sequence, given any natural number $N$, there exists an index $n_0$ such that if $p, q \geqslant n_0$ then $|a_p - a_q| < 1/2N$.

Similarly, since $s = \lim\limits_{m \to \infty} a_{n_m}$, there exists an index $m_0$ so large that if $m \geqslant m_0$ then $|s - a_{n_m}| < 1/2N$; actually, we may take $m_0$ such that $n_{m_0} \geqslant n_0$.

It follows that, taking $n \geqslant n_0$ and using $m \geqslant m_0$, we have

$$|s - a_n| = |(s - a_{n_m}) + (a_{n_m} - a_n)| \leqslant |s - a_{n_m}| + |a_{n_m} - a_n|$$
$$< 1/2N + 1/2N = 1/N.$$

As $N$ is arbitrary, this proves that $S = \lim\limits_{n \to \infty} a_n$.

*Note.* We repeat for emphasis the meaning of the Cauchy convergence criterion. It states that sequences of *real* numbers, whose terms of sufficiently large index concentrate in arbitrarily small intervals, must necessarily be convergent sequences. Thus, it states the *existence* of a real number which is the limit of the sequence.

It is important to stress that the sequences in question are sequences of *real* numbers. This criterion shows exactly that *the set of real numbers is* COMPLETE in the sense that *it contains the limit of every fundamental sequence*; in other words, the set of real numbers does not have gaps.

But, how about the set of *rational* numbers?

We have seen in Chapter 3 that *the set of rational numbers is not complete,* as it does not have enough numbers to guarantee that every fundamental sequence of rational numbers has a limit which is a rational number. We know that there exist fundamental sequences of rational numbers which define irrational numbers, that is, their limit is not a rational number. To complete the set of rational numbers means to define the real numbers, adjoining the irrational ones to the rational ones and, thus, insuring that any fundamental sequence of rational numbers will now have a (possibly irrational) limit.

Since the set of real numbers is complete, by Cauchy's theorem, we are sure that a repetition of Cantor's construction, as done in Chapter 3, and *starting with real numbers* (instead of with the rational numbers), will not lead to any new kind of numbers.

## A Convention

Usually we introduce a very useful convention to describe the behavior of certain divergent sequences.

For example, the sequence $2, 4, 8, \ldots, 2^n, \ldots$ is not convergent. However, given any neighborhood $U_N$ of plus infinity, that is, given any half-line $(N, +\infty)$, there exists an index $n_0$ such that if $n \geqslant n_0$ then $a_n = 2^n \in (N, +\infty)$. Thus, for example, if $N = 1000$ then, for $n \geqslant n_0 = 10$, we have $a_n = 2^n \geqslant 2^{10} = 1024 > 1000 = N$.

It may be easily checked that if $+\infty$ should be a real number, then the above sequence will be satisfying a property, exactly analogous to the one expressing that $\lim a_n = s$, replacing, however, $s$ by $+\infty$; given any neighborhood $U_N$ of $+\infty$, there exists a neighborhood $U_{N_0}$ of $+\infty$ (in the set of natural integers), such that if $n \in U_{n_0}$ then $a_n \in U_N$.

Thus, because of this analogy, it is natural to say that the above sequence converges to $+\infty$, and to write $\lim 2^n = +\infty$.

Let us complete the definition for the general case.

(1) The sequence $(a_n)$ *tends to plus infinity* when, given any integer $N > 0$, as large as we like, there exists $n_0$ such that if $n \geqslant n_0$ then $a_n > N$. We use the notation $\lim a_n = +\infty$.

(2) The sequence $(a_n)$ *tends to minus infinity* when the sequence $(-a_n)$ tends to plus infinity. That is, given arbitrarily the integer $N > 0$, there

exists an index $n_0$ such that if $n \geqslant n_0$ then $a_n < - N$. We use the notation $\lim a_n = - \infty$.

We must, however, bear in mind that, even though we agree that the sequence $(a_n)$ tends (or converges) to $+ \infty$, or $- \infty$, it is in fact a divergent sequence, in agreement with the terminology previously introduced.

### Some Important Limits

We cannot conclude this chapter without treating some of the important limits that appear most commonly in the calculus.

First we establish the following result.

*If $1 + k > 0$ then $(1 + k)^n \geqslant 1 + nk$ for every natural integer $n$.*

Indeed, this inequality is trivial for $n = 1$. To prove it for every natural integer, by the principle of finite induction we shall assume that it is valid for a certain integer $n$ and deduce that it is also true for $n + 1$.

In fact, from $(1 + k)^n \geqslant 1 + nk$, it follows that

$$(1 + k)^{n+1} = (1 + k)^n \cdot (1 + k) \geqslant (1 + nk) \cdot (1 + k)$$
$$= 1 + (n + 1)k + nk^2 \geqslant 1 + (n + 1)k$$

because $1 + k > 0$ and $k^2 \geqslant 0$. Therefore, by the principle of finite induction, we have $(1 + k)^n \geqslant 1 + nk$ for every natural integer $n$.

EXAMPLE 1. If $p$ is a fixed positive real number, then

$$\lim p^n = \begin{cases} + \infty & \text{when } 1 < p \\ 1 & \text{when } p = 1 \\ 0 & \text{when } 0 \leqslant p < 1 \end{cases}$$

First, let us consider the case where $1 < p$, thus $p = 1 + k$, with $k > 0$.

We show that for every integer $N > 0$ there exists an integer $n_0$ such that if $n \geqslant n_0$ then $p^n > N$; this means that $\lim p^n = + \infty$. For this purpose we use the Archimedean property of real numbers; since $k > 0$, given $N$ there exists an integer $n_0$ such that $n_0 k > N - 1$. Therefore, using the inequality obtained above, we have $p^{n_0} = (1 + k)^{n_0} \geqslant 1 + n_0 k > N$.

Finally, from $p > 1$, it follows that the sequence $(p^n)$ is monotone strictly increasing; hence, if $n \geqslant n_0$, we have $p^n \geqslant p^{n_0} > N$.

If $p = 1$, the result is trivial.

Now consider the case where $0 \leqslant p < 1$; we may assume that $p \neq 0$, otherwise it is trivial.

Let $q = 1/p$, so $1 < q$; then $p^n = 1/q^n$ and $\lim q^n = + \infty$; that is, given any natural number $N$, there exists an index $n_0$ such that if $n \geqslant n_0$ then $q^n > N$. Thus, $p^n < 1/N$ for every $n \geqslant n_0$, which means that $\lim p^n = 0$.

EXAMPLE 2. If $p$ is a fixed number, $p > 0$, then $\lim \sqrt[n]{p} = 1$.

The result is trivial when $p = 1$. We assume that $p \neq 1$.

Let $a_n = \sqrt[n]{p} - 1$, so $1 + a_n > 0$ and, therefore, $(1 + a_n)^n \geqslant 1 + na_n$ for every index $n \geqslant 1$.

If $p > 1$ then $\sqrt[n]{p} > 1$, so $\sqrt[n]{p} - 1 = a_n > 0$ and, therefore, $p = (1 + a_n)^n \geqslant 1 + n.a_n$; thus $0 < a_n \leqslant (p - 1)/n$ for every index $n$. Letting $b_n = (p - 1)/n$, we have $\lim b_n = 0$, hence $\lim a_n = 0$ and, thus, $\lim \sqrt[n]{p} = 1 + \lim a_n = 1$.

If $p < 1$, we let $q = 1/p > 1$; by what we have proved, $\lim \sqrt[n]{q} = 1$, hence

$$\lim \sqrt[n]{p} = \lim \sqrt[n]{\frac{1}{q}} = \frac{1}{\lim \sqrt[n]{q}} = 1.$$

EXAMPLE 3. $\lim \sqrt[n]{n} = 1$.

Since $n \geqslant 1$, we have $\sqrt[n]{n} \geqslant 1$. We must show that for every integer $N$ there exists an index $n_0$ such that if $n \geqslant n_0$ then $\sqrt[n]{n} < 1 + 1/N$.

If this were not the case, then there would exist an integer $N$ with the property $\sqrt[n]{n} \geqslant 1 + 1/N$ for indices $n$ as large as we like (for example, $n \geqslant 1 + 2N^2$).

Using the Newton binomial expansion, with $n \geqslant 2$, we have

$$n \geqslant \left(1 + \frac{1}{N}\right)^n = 1 + n \cdot \frac{1}{N} + \frac{n(n-1)}{2} \cdot \frac{1}{N^2} + \ldots + \frac{1}{N^n} > \frac{n(n-1)}{2} \cdot \frac{1}{N^2}$$

This implies that $n - 1 < 2N^2$, hence $n < 1 + 2N^2$, which is a contradiction. Therefore, it must be true that $\lim \sqrt[n]{n} = 1$.

EXAMPLE 4. If $p$ is a fixed real number, $p > 0$, then

$$\lim \frac{p^n}{n} = \begin{cases} \infty & \text{when } p > 1 \\ 0 & \text{when } 0 \leqslant p \leqslant 1. \end{cases}$$

First, consider the case where $p > 1$, hence $p = 1 + x$, with $x > 0$. Then, for every index $n \geqslant 2$,

$$p^n = (1 + x)^n = 1 + nx + \frac{n(n-1)}{2}x^2 + \ldots + x^n > \frac{n(n-1)}{2}x^2$$

therefore

$$\frac{p^n}{n} > (n - 1)\frac{x^2}{2}.$$

Letting $b_n = (x^2/2).(n - 1)$, we have $\lim b_n = \infty$, hence $\lim p^n/n = \infty$.

Now we assume that $p \leqslant 1$. Then $\lim p^n = 0$ and $\lim 1/n = 0$, hence $\lim p^n/n = 0$.

EXAMPLE 5. The sequence $(a_n)$, whose general term is $a_n = (1 + 1/n)^n$, is monotone strictly increasing and bounded above. Therefore, it is convergent, and its limit is a real number, denoted by $e$; we have $2 < e < 3$.

We have $a_n < a_{n+1}$ for every index $n$. Indeed,

$$\frac{a_{n+1}}{a_n} = \frac{\left(1 + \dfrac{1}{n+1}\right)^{n+1}}{\left(1 + \dfrac{1}{n}\right)^n} = \left(1 + \frac{1}{n+1}\right)\left[\frac{\left(1 + \dfrac{1}{n+1}\right)\left(1 - \dfrac{1}{n+1}\right)}{\left(1 + \dfrac{1}{n}\right)\left(1 - \dfrac{1}{n+1}\right)}\right]^n$$

$$= \left(1 + \frac{1}{n+1}\right)\left(1 - \frac{1}{(n+1)^2}\right)^n$$

because

$$\left(1 + \frac{1}{n}\right)\left(1 - \frac{1}{n+1}\right) = 1.$$

Since

$$\left(1 - \frac{1}{(n+1)^2}\right)^n \geq 1 - n\frac{1}{(n+1)^2}$$

by the inequality previously proved (page 55), we have

$$\frac{a_{n+1}}{a_n} \geq \left(1 + \frac{1}{n+1}\right)\left(1 - \frac{n}{(n+1)^2}\right) = 1 + \frac{1}{(n+1)^3} > 1$$

Now we shall show that the sequence $(a_n)$ is bounded above. We have, by the binomial expansion,

$$\left(1 + \frac{1}{n}\right)^n = 1 + n \cdot \frac{1}{n} + \frac{n(n-1)}{1 \cdot 2} \cdot \frac{1}{n^2} + \frac{n(n-1)(n-2)}{1 \cdot 2 \cdot 3} \cdot \frac{1}{n^3}$$

$$+ \ldots + \frac{1}{n^n} = 1 + 1 + \frac{1}{2!}\left(1 - \frac{1}{n}\right) + \frac{1}{3!}\left(1 - \frac{1}{n}\right)\left(1 + \frac{2}{n}\right)$$

$$+ \ldots + \frac{1}{n!}\left(1 - \frac{1}{n}\right)\left(1 - \frac{2}{n}\right)\cdots\left(1 - \frac{n-1}{n}\right)$$

$$< 1 + 1 + \left(\frac{1}{2} + \frac{1}{2^2} + \ldots + \frac{1}{2^{n-1}}\right) < 3$$

because

$$\frac{1}{k!} \leq \frac{1}{2^{k-1}}$$

and

$$\frac{1}{2} + \frac{1}{2^2} + \ldots + \frac{1}{2^{n-1}} < 1$$

for every index $n \geq 2$.

Therefore, the bounded monotone increasing sequence $(a_n)$ has limit between 2 and 3.

Later we shall return to the number $e$ and determine one of its nice properties.

EXAMPLE 6. Definition of $x^\alpha$, where $x > 0$ and $\alpha$ are any real numbers.

In Chapter 3 (page 25), we defined the rational power of a strictly positive real number. Now, using properties of limits of sequences, we shall define the symbol $x^\alpha$, where $x > 0$ and $\alpha$ are any real numbers.

It is sufficient to consider the case where $x > 1$. For, if $x = 1$, we define $1^\alpha = 1$ for every real number $\alpha$. If $0 < x < 1$, we define $x^\alpha = (1/x)^\alpha$, noticing that $1/x > 1$ and, therefore, the expression $(1/x)^\alpha$ would have been already defined.

Consider a sequence $(a_n)$ of rational numbers, which is monotone strictly increasing and such that $\lim a_n = \alpha$; such sequences clearly exist, as we notice when considering for every natural integer $n$ a rational number $a_n$ such that $\alpha - 1/n < a_n < \alpha - 1/(n + 1)$.

From $a_n < a_{n+1}$, it follows that $x^{a_n} < x^{a_{n+1}}$ (this is easy to verify, since $a_n, a_{n+1}$ are rational numbers). Therefore, the sequence of real numbers $(x^{a_n})$ is monotone strictly increasing. It is bounded above, for example, by any real number $x^b$ where $\alpha < b$ and $b$ is a rational number.

Thus, the bounded monotone sequence $(x^{a_n})$ has limit, let us say $\beta = \lim x^{a_n}$.

We define $x^a = \beta$. However, even though this definition may seem natural, it still needs to be justified. Indeed, we must show that if $(a'_n)$ is any other sequence of rational numbers such that $\lim a'_n = \alpha$, then again the limit of the sequence $(x^{a'_n})$ exists, and it is also equal to $\beta$. This means that the number $\beta$, thus obtained, will be independent of the particular sequence approaching $\alpha$.

Let us perform the needed verification. If $(a'_n)$ is a sequence such that $\lim a'_n = \alpha$, letting $b_n = a'_n - a_n$, then $(b_n)$ is a null sequence. Moreover, $x^{a'_n} = x^{a_n}.x^{b_n}$, and it will be sufficient to prove that $\lim x^{b_n} = 1$ for every null sequence $(b_n)$ of rational numbers.

We first assume that every rational number $b_n$ is positive. Explicitly, given any natural number $N$, we must show the existence of $n_0$ such that if $n \geqslant n_0$ then $1 \leqslant x^{b_n} < 1 + 1/N$ (because $1 < x$ and $b_n \geqslant 0$). Let $M$ be an integer so large that $M > x.N$. Since $(b_n)$ is a null sequence, there exists an integer $n_0$ such that if $n \geqslant n_0$ then $0 \leqslant b_n < 1/M$. Therefore $1 \leqslant x^{b_n} < x^{1/M}$.

Now, from the inequality shown on page 55, we have

$$\left(1 + \frac{x}{M}\right)^M \geqslant 1 + x > x;$$

hence

$$1 + \frac{x}{M} \geqslant x^{1/M}$$

and thus

$$1 < x^{b_n} < 1 + \frac{x}{M} < 1 + \frac{1}{N}.$$

In the general case of any null sequence $(b_n)$, we have

$$\frac{1}{x^{|b_n|}} = \left(\frac{1}{x}\right)^{|b_n|} = x^{-|b_n|} \leq x^{b_n} \leq x^{|b_n|}$$

Since the sequence $(|b_n|)$ is a null sequence of positive terms, we have

$$1 = \lim \frac{1}{x^{|b_n|}} \leqslant \lim x^{b_n} \leqslant \lim x^{|b_n|} = 1$$

that is, $\lim x^{b_n} = 1$.

This proves our assertion, and justifies the definition of $x^\alpha$, when $x > 0$ and $\alpha$ are any real numbers.

We shall see in Chapter 9 how it is possible, using theoretical results on uniformly continuous functions, to define $x^\alpha$ (for $x > 0$, $\alpha$ real numbers), without requiring any verification such as the proof just given.

### Exercises

1. Determine the general term of each of the sequences given below by their initial terms.
   (a) $0, -1/9, 4/16 = 1/4, -9/25, 16/36 = 4/9, \ldots$
   (b) $2, 5/2, 10/3, 17/4, 26/5, 37/6, \ldots$
   (c) $0, 1/6, 1/3, 9/20, 8/15, 25/42, 9/14, 49/72, 32/45, \ldots$

2. Consider the sequence, whose general term is

$$a_n = \frac{n-1}{n+1}$$

and the following property $P_n$:

$$1 - a_n < 0.0001$$

Show that $P_n$ is true for every sufficiently large index $n$. Determine the smallest index $n_0$ for which the property is valid.

3. Consider the sequence, whose general term is

$$a_n = \frac{1000 \cdot (1 + (-1)^n)}{n},$$

and the property $P_n$: $a_n < 1$.

Show that this property is true for arbitrarily large values of $n$: if this is the case, determine the smallest index $n_0$ for which the property is true.

4. Consider the sequence whose general term is $a_n = (-1)^n.(1000 - n)$ and the property $P_n: a_n > 1$.

Show that $P_n$ is true for arbitrarily large values of $n$, but not for all sufficiently large $n$.

5. Determine the limits (possibly $+\infty$ or $-\infty$) of the following sequences, given by their general term.

(a) $\dfrac{n-1}{n+1}$

(b) $(-1)^n \cdot \dfrac{1}{n}$

(c) $1 + (-1)^n \cdot \dfrac{1}{n}$

(d) $\dfrac{n^2 - 1}{n^2 + 1}$

(e) $\dfrac{n^5 - 3n^3 + 5n}{n^6 + 4n^4 + 2n^2 + 1}$

(f) $(-1)^n + \dfrac{1}{n}$

(g) $3.(-1)^n + 5$
(h) $(-1)^n.n + 1000000$
(i) $n.(1 + (-1)^n)$
(j) $n^2 + (-1)^n.2n$

(k) $\sqrt{n+1} - \sqrt{n}$

(l) $\dfrac{n}{2^n}$

(m) $(\sqrt{n+1} - \sqrt{n}).\sqrt{n + \dfrac{1}{2}}$

(n) $\dfrac{n^5}{2^n}$

(p) $\sqrt[n]{n^2}$

(q) $\dfrac{1^2 + 2^2 + \ldots + n^2}{n^3}$

(r) $\dfrac{n!}{n^n}$

6. Determine the limit of the sequence whose initial terms are $\sqrt{2}$, $\sqrt{2\sqrt{2}}$, $\sqrt{2\sqrt{2\sqrt{2}}}$, ...

7. Prove that if the sequence $(a_n)$ has limit, $\lim a_n = s$, then the sequence $(b_n)$ with general term

$$b_n = \frac{a_1 + \ldots + a_n}{n}$$

("arithmetical mean" of the terms $a_n$) is also convergent to the same limit: $\lim b_n = s$.

8. Prove that if the sequence $(a_n)$ with all terms $a_n > 0$ has limit $\lim a_n = s$, then the sequence $(b_n)$ with $b_n = (a_1 a_2 \ldots a_n)^{1/n}$ ("geometrical mean" of the terms $a_n$) is also convergent to the same limit: $\lim b_n = s$.

9. Prove that if the sequences $(a_n)$, $(b_n)$ have limit, $\lim a_n = s$, $\lim b_n = t$, then the sequence $(c_n)$, whose general term is

$$c_n = \frac{a_1 b_1 + a_2 b_2 + \ldots + a_n b_n}{n}$$

has limit, $\lim c_n = s.t.$

10. Use Cauchy's convergence criterion to show the convergence of the sequence whose general term is $a_n = (n+1)/n$.

11. Determine the limit of the sequence whose general term is

$$a_n = \frac{1}{1 \cdot 2} + \frac{1}{2 \cdot 3} + \frac{1}{3 \cdot 4} + \ldots + \frac{1}{n \cdot (n+1)}$$

# 6

# Functions

In Chapter 1, where we introduced the notions of set and correspondence, we mentioned that the name FUNCTION would be reserved for special types of correspondences. We wish to emphasize that this distinction between correspondences and functions is purely a matter of convention, and may vary with different authors.

Using $X$, $Y$ as two sets of real numbers, let us give a rule or correspondence which assigns to each real number $x$ in the set $X$, a real number $y$ in $Y$. Such a correspondence is called a FUNCTION, *defined on the set $X$, with values in the set $Y$*. We say also that it is a *function from $X$ into $Y$*.

The notation $y = f(x)$ will indicate that the rule or correspondence or function $f$ associates to $x$ the value $y$.

The set $X$ is called the DOMAIN OF DEFINITION of the function; those elements of $Y$ which are values of the function constitute a set, called the RANGE OF VALUES of the function.

Before giving examples, we make a brief preliminary comment.

In more advanced studies there will appear, in a natural way, correspondences that to each element of a set will associate *more than one* element of another set. These correspondences are traditionally called MULTI-VALUED FUNCTIONS; however, this terminology should be avoided, since it leads to ambiguity.

The functions which will be considered here are exclusively SINGLE-VALUED FUNCTIONS: to every $x$ of $X$ they associate *one and only one* value $y$ in $Y$.

## Examples of Functions

EXAMPLE 1. A sequence of real numbers is, by definition, a correspondence that associates to every natural integer $n$ a real number $a_n$. Thus, the correspondence $n \rightarrow a_n$, from the set of natural numbers (which are special real numbers) into the set of real numbers, is a function; the domain of definition is the set of natural numbers; the range of values is the set of terms $a_n$.

Let us point out that the notation $a_n$ is as good as $f(n)$; both express a dependency on the natural number $n$.

Since the name "sequence" has been already reserved for the type of functions described in the above example, the word function will not be used in the case of sequences.

EXAMPLE 2. The correspondence that associates to each real number $x$ the same number $x$ is a function, defined on the set of all the real numbers, with range equal to the same set.

Usually, we have some idea of the nature of the function by means of its GRAPHIC REPRESENTATION. For this purpose, we draw two lines in the plane, which cross at a point 0, in right angles. We orient these lines by fixing, at will, the positive sense in each of these lines. In each line we choose, in an arbitrary way, a unit of length. Thus, summarizing, we introduce in the plane, a system of *cartesian orthogonal coordinates*, these lines being called the $x$ *axis* and the $y$ *axis*.

If $x \rightarrow y = f(x)$ is the given function, then its *graph* (in this system of coordinates) is the set of points of the plane, with coordinates $(x, f(x))$.

Thus, the graph of the function in this example is quite simple, as is shown in Figure 1.

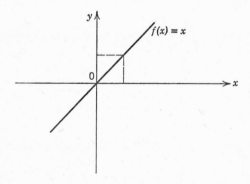

Figure 1

EXAMPLE 3. Power functions (with integral exponents $n > 0$): $f(x) = x^n$.

The domain of these functions is the set of real numbers; the range depends on whether $n$ is an even or an odd integer. If $n$ is even, the range of the function is $[0, +\infty)$; if $n$ is odd, the range of the function is the set of real numbers.

EXAMPLE 4. Power functions (with negative integral exponents $-n \leqslant 0$):
$f(x) = x^{-n}$.

Such functions are not defined for $x = 0$. If $n = 0$, the range is just the set consisting only of the number 1, since $f(x) = x^0 = 1$, for every $x \neq 0$. If $n \neq 0$ is even, the range is $(0, +\infty)$; if $n$ is odd, the range is the set of real numbers different from 0.

The graphs of such functions as $f(x) = x^{-1} = 1/x$, $f(x) = x^{-2} = 1/x^2$, $f(x) = x^{-3} = 1/x^3$, may be drawn as an exercise.

EXAMPLE 5. Polynomial functions: let

$$P = a_0 X^n + a_1 X^{n-1} + a_2 X^{n-2} + \ldots + a_{n-1} X + a_n$$

be a polynomial with real coefficients, where $X$ is an indeterminate, that is, just a symbol about which nothing else is said. The correspondence that associates to every real number $x$ the real number

$$P(x) = a_0 x^n + a_1 x^{n-1} + a_2 x^{n-2} + \ldots + a_{n-1} x + a_n$$

is called a *polynomial function*.

Examples are

$x \rightarrow P(x) = 3x + 2$, which is a LINEAR function;

$x \rightarrow P(x) = 5x^2 - 3x + 2$, which is a SECOND DEGREE TRINOMIAL;

$x \rightarrow P(x) = x^5 - 4x^3 + 7x^2 - 3x + 8$, which is a polynomial function of degree 5.

The domain of definition of a polynomial function is the set of all real numbers. In each concrete case, it is not a difficult problem to investigate the range of a polynomial function, as it is proposed in some exercises.

We point out the following property of polynomials.

*For every polynomial function of degree $n > 0$, there exist at most $n$ distinct real numbers on which the value of the function is 0*; each such number is therefore called a ZERO or ROOT of the polynomial function.

In this proof we shall use the principle of finite induction, as stated on page 4. To show that our statement is true for every natural number $n$, we first notice that it is true when $n = 1$. Indeed, let $P = a_0 X + a_1$, with $a_0 \neq 0$ (that is, $P$ has degree 1); then $x = -a_1/a_0$ is a zero for the polynomial function, and it is clearly the only one.

Next we assume that every polynomial $Q$ of degree $n - 1$ has at most $n - 1$ distinct zeros; we shall prove that the polynomial $P$, of degree $n$, has at most $n$ distinct zeros.

Indeed, let $P = a_0 X^n + a_1 X^{n-1} + \ldots + a_n$ be a given polynomial of degree $n > 0$, and assume that $x_1$ is a real number such that $P(x_1) = 0$. As we know from elementary algebra, by division of $P$ by $X - x_1$, we obtain a quotient $Q$ and a remainder $R$, which are polynomials such that $Q$ has degree $n - 1$ and $R$ has degree less than 1 (degree of $X - x_1$); moreover, they are the only polynomials with such properties. Thus,

$$P = (X - x_1).Q + R,$$

where $R$ has degree zero, that is, $R$ is a real number, let us say $R = r$. Therefore, the value of this polynomial function at the real number $x_1$ is $0 = P(x_1) = (x_1 - x_1).Q(x_1) + r = r$. Thus, $P = (X - x_1).Q$, where $Q$ has degree $n - 1$.

In summary, every root $x_1$ of $P$ determines a polynomial $Q$ of degree $n - 1$ such that $P = (X - x_1).Q$. Any other root $x_2$ of $P$, distinct from $x_1$, must be a root of $Q$: $0 = P(x_2) = (x_2 - x_1).Q(x_2)$, with $x_2 \neq x_1$, so $Q(x_2) = 0$. Conversely, every root of $Q$ is a root of $P = (X - x_1).Q$.

By our induction hypothesis, since $Q$ has degree $n - 1$, it has at most $n - 1$ distinct zeros; hence $P$ has at most $n$ distinct roots.

By the principle of finite induction, the proposition is therefore true for every natural number.

EXAMPLE 6. Rational functions: let

$$\frac{P}{Q} = \frac{a_0 X^n + a_1 X^{n-1} + \ldots + a_n}{b_0 X^m + b_1 X^{m-1} + \ldots + b_m},$$

where $m$, $n$ are positive integers (and not every coefficient $b_i$ is 0); then $P/Q$ is called a *rational fraction*. The correspondence that associates to every real number $x$, for which $Q(x) \neq 0$, the real number

$$\frac{P(x)}{Q(x)} = \frac{a_0 x^n + a_1 x^{n-1} + \ldots + a_{n-1} x + a_n}{b_0 x^m + b_1 x^{m-1} + \ldots + b_{m-1} x + b_m},$$

is called a *rational function*. This rational function is not defined at the values $x$ for which $Q(x) = 0$.

Examples 2, 3, 4, and 5 are merely particular cases of the last one.

For those who know some trigonometry, we give the following examples.

EXAMPLE 7. The correspondences $x \rightarrow \sin x$, $x \rightarrow \cos x$, etc., are real valued functions, defined on the real line; the range of values of both functions is the interval $[-1, 1]$.

These functions *are not* rational functions. It is not sufficient merely to note that they do not look like rational functions; we must in fact show that there exist some property satisfied by these functions, but not true for the rational functions. We know that there exist infinitely many values of $x$ for which $\sin x = 0$, $\cos x = 0$. On the other hand, the values of $x$ for which $P(x)/Q(x) = 0$ must be such that $P(x) = 0$, $Q(x) \neq 0$; as we proved before, there are only finitely many real numbers $x$ for which $P(x) = 0$.

*Note.* In Example 7, we mentioned the trigonometric functions sine and cosine. It is easy to recall how they are introduced in trigonometry. One considers in the plane a circle (Figure 2) with center in a point 0 and radius 1 (the unit circle); if $x$ is a real number such that $0 \leqslant x < 2\pi$, if

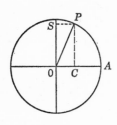

the angle $AOP$ has measure $x$ in radians, then the length of $\overline{OS}$ is the value sin $x$, while the length of $\overline{OC}$ is the value cos $x$. More generally, if $x$ is now any real number, then it is between convenient integral multiples of $2\pi$, for example, $k.2\pi \leqslant x < (k+1).2\pi$; hence, $0 < x - k.2\pi < 2\pi$; then, we define sin $x$ = sin $(x - k.2\pi)$, cos $x$ = cos $(x - k.2\pi)$.

Our point is that these definitions use many concepts that are extraneous to analysis. There-

**Figure 2**

fore, in trying to lay the foundations of analysis on solid ground, it is not legitimate to accept such definitions. We should reject functions such as sine and cosine, unless we may find purely analytical means for defining them. Happily enough, this is the case: by means of POWER SERIES (which is beyond the scope of this book), it is possible to define the trigonometric and many more functions currently found in calculus.

Nevertheless, since these functions may be correctly defined, we shall not hesitate to quote them as examples.

Actually, we have defined in a rigorous way only comparatively few functions: those that are obtained from the operations with real numbers (sum, subtraction, multiplication, division), applied in any order, a finite number of times — therefore, none other than rational functions.

Now, we describe two methods to create new functions from given ones: the notions of "function of a function" and "inverse function."

Let $f$ be a function defined on a set $X$ of real numbers, having range contained in a set $Y$ of real numbers; thus, to each real number $x$ in $X$ the function $f$ associates the value $y = f(x)$, belonging to $Y$.

Let $g$ be a function defined on the set $Y$ considered above, with values in a set $Z$ of real numbers; thus, to each element $y$ in $Y$ the function $g$ associates the value $z = g(y)$ in $Z$.

Now, we consider the following correspondence, obtained by "composing" the correspondences $f$, $g$: to each $x$ in $X$ we associate the real number $g(f(x))$, equal to the image by $g$ of the image of $x$ by $f$. This is a correspondence from the set $X$ into the set $Z$; it is therefore a function defined on $X$ with values in the set $Z$. This function is said to be COMPOSED OF $f$ FOLLOWED BY $g$. It is denoted by $g \circ f$. We say also that $g \circ f$ is a FUNCTION OF A FUNCTION OF $x$.

EXAMPLES. (*1*) Let $f$, $g$ be the functions given by

$$y = f(x) = x^2, \text{ for every real number } x,$$

$$z = g(y) = \sin y, \text{ for every real number } y.$$

Since the range of $f$ is contained in the domain of $g$, we may consider the function $g \circ f$, given by $g \circ f(x) = \sin f(x) = \sin x^2$, for every real number $x$.

(*2*) Let $f$, $g$ be the functions given by

$$v = f(x) = 1 - x^2, \text{ for every } x \in [-1, 1],$$

$$z = g(y) = \sqrt{y}, \text{ for every } y \geqslant 0.$$

Since the range of $f$ is contained in the domain of $g$, we may consider the function $g \circ f$, given by $g \circ f(x) = \sqrt{1 - x^2}$, defined for every $x$ in the closed interval $[-1, 1]$.

We now introduce the concept of a function, inverse to a given function. Let $f$ be a real valued function, defined in a set $X$ of real numbers, having range equal to a set $Y$ of real numbers; in other words, to every real number $x$ in $X$, the function $f$ associates a real number $y = f(x)$, and we may obtain all the real numbers of $Y$ in this manner. Usually, it happens that some number $y$ is the value of $f$ at two distinct points $x_1$, $x_2$: $f(x_1) = f(x_2) = y$. For example, this is true for the function $f(x) = x^2$, since two numbers, which differ only by their sign, have the same square.

Here, *we assume that this is not the case*, that is, the function $f$ is such that if $x_1$, $x_2$ are distinct real numbers, then $f(x_1)$, $f(x_2)$ are also distinct. In other words, the correspondence $f$ is one-to-one, in the sense of the definition in Chapter 1.

This being true, we define the INVERSE FUNCTION $g$ of $f$ in the following way: $g$ is the function which associates to each real number $y$ in $Y$ the unique real number $x$ in $X$, such that $f(x) = y$. Therefore, if $y = f(x)$ then $g(y) = g(f(x)) = x$ and, similarly, if $x = g(y)$ then $f(g(y)) = f(x) = y$.

Clearly the domain of definition of the inverse function $g$ is equal to the range of values of $f$, and the range of values of $g$ is equal to the domain of definition of $f$.

EXAMPLE. Let $f$ be the function $f(x) = x - 3$, which is obtained by subtracting 3 from each real number $x$; thus, $f$ has domain and range of values equal to the whole set of real numbers; moreover, it is a one-to-one function. Its graph is shown as Figure 3.

The inverse function $g$ is the one that consists of adding 3 to each real number $x$. Thus, if $y = x - 3$, then $g(y) = y + 3 = x$.

Note that this function $g(y) = y + 3$ may also be written $g(x) = x + 3$, or $g(z) = z + 3$, etc., since all these ways indicate only "to add 3 to each real number."

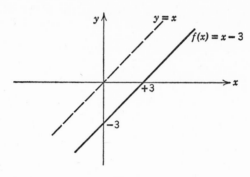

Figure 3

The graph of *g* is shown as Figure 4.

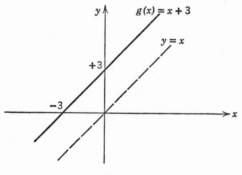

Figure 4

By superposing the graphs of the two functions $f(x)$, $g(x)$, we see that they are symmetrical with respect to the bissector $y = x$ of the angle between the co-ordinate axis.

This is a general fact, since the points of the graph of the function *f* are those having co-ordinates $(x, f(x))$, while the points of the graph of the function *g* are those with co-ordinates $(y, g(y))$. Now, if $y = f(x)$, we have $g(y) = g(f(x)) = x$, hence the points of the graph of *g* have coordinates $(f(x), x)$; therefore, they are symmetrical, with respect to the line $y = x$, to the points of the graph of *f* (Figure 3).

ANOTHER EXAMPLE. Let *f* be this function: to each real number $x \geqslant 0$, *f* associates its square $f(x) = x^2$. This function is defined on the set of all positive real numbers, with a range of values equal to the set of all positive real numbers. It is a one-to-one function, since distinct *positive* numbers have distinct squares.

The function $g$, inverse of $f$, is defined on the set of all positive real numbers, and has a range of values equal to this same set. Precisely, $g$ is the function that associates to each positive real number its positive square root: $g(y) = + \sqrt{y}$.

The graphs of $f$ and $g$ are drawn in Figure 5.

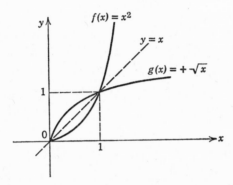

**Figure 5**

Note that in this example, we have defined the inverse of the function $f$, given by $f(x) = x^2$, *for every* $x \geqslant 0$.

Why did we not consider the function $\tilde{f}$, given by the same rule, $\tilde{f}(x) = x^2$, but defined instead for every real number $x$, whether positive or negative?*

The reason is very simple. Since $f(-x) = f(x) = x^2$, in trying to define an inverse function $g$ for $\tilde{f}$, we would only obtain a multivalued correspondence, the one that to each positive real number associates the pair of its square roots; this is a pair of real numbers, but not one real number, and thus this correspondence is not a function with real values. Of course, we may choose to consider only the positive square root (or the negative one). With each one of these choices, kept fixed, we define what is traditionally called a *branch of the inverse multivalued correspondence* $g$. Thus, in this case, $g$ has two branches (Figure 6).

We conclude these considerations on inverse functions with an important case in which there exists, surely, the inverse function.

*If $f$ is a monotone strictly increasing or strictly decreasing function, then there exists the inverse function of $f$, which is of the same type, respectively, monotone strictly increasing, or monotone strictly decreasing function.*

---

* Even though the functions $f$, $\tilde{f}$, are defined by the same rule, which consists of associating with a number $x$ its square, they are not considered the same function because their domains of definition are distinct. We say that $f$ is the RESTRICTION of $\tilde{f}$ to the smaller domain of positive real numbers.

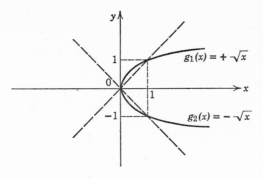

**Figure 6**

The new terms "monotone strictly increasing function," "monotone strictly decreasing function," and similar ones have the same meaning as in the case of sequences. A function $f$ is MONOTONE INCREASING when: if $x_1 < x_2$ then $f(x_1) \leqslant f(x_2)$; and MONOTONE STRICTLY INCREASING when: if $x_1 < x_2$ then $f(x_1) < f(x_2)$. The same is true for MONOTONE STRICTLY DECREASING and MONOTONE DECREASING functions.

With these definitions, the above assertion becomes clear. For, if $f$ is monotone strictly increasing, then $f$ is a one-to-one correspondence from its domain of definition to its range of values. Therefore, there exists the inverse function $g$. If $x_1 < x_2$ implies $f(x_1) < f(x_2)$ then $g$ is also strictly increasing for this reason: if $y_1 < y_2$, let $x_1$, $x_2$ be such that $y_1 = f(x_1)$, $y_2 = f(x_2)$; if $g(y_1) \geqslant g(y_2)$, that is $x_1 \geqslant x_2$, it follows that $y_1 = f(x_1) \geqslant f(x_2) = y_2$, a contradiction. Hence $g(y_1) < g(y_2)$, which proves that $g$ is also a strictly increasing function. A similar argument is used for strictly decreasing functions.

### Exercises

1. Draw the graph of each of the following functions; in each case, determine the domain of definition and range of values.

(a) $f(x) = 3 \sin 2x + 5$

(b) $f(x) = 5 \cos (3x - \pi/2)$

(c) $f(x) = 2 \cos (x + \pi/3)$

(d) $f(x) = \tan x - x$

(e) $f(x) = \sqrt{|x|}$

(f) $f(x) = x^2 - 2 |x|$

(g) $f(x) = |x - 1| + |x + 1| - 2$

(h) $f(x) = x^3 - 3x + 1$
(i) $f(x) = x^2(x - 1)$
(j) $f(x) = x + 1/x$
(k) $f(x) = x(1 - x)^2$
(l) $f(x) = 3x^3 + 2x - 1/x$
(m) $f(x) = \sqrt[3]{x - 1}$
(n) $f(x) = (x^2 + 1)/(x^2 - 1)$
(o) $f(x) = + \sqrt{4 - x^2}$
(p) $f(x) = \sin^2 x$
(q) $f(x) = \cos^2 x$
(r) $f(x) = x + \sin x$
(s) $f(x) = x \cdot \sin x$
(t) $f(x) = \sin x/x$
(u) $f(x) = \sin (1/x)$
(v) $f(x) = x \cdot \sin (1/x)$
(w) $f(x) = (1/x) \cdot \sin (1/x)$
(x) $f(x) = x^2 \cdot \sin (1/x)$
(y) $f(x) = (1/x^2) \cdot \sin (1/x)$
(z) $f(x) = \tan x$

2. State which of the functions in the preceding exercise are monotone, increasing, decreasing, strictly increasing, or strictly decreasing.

3. Let $[x]$ denote the largest integer $n$ such that $n \leqslant x$. Draw the graphs of the following functions.
   (a) $f(x) = [x]$
   (b) $f(x) = x - [x]$
   (c) $f(x) = + \sqrt{x - [x]}$
   (d) $f(x) = [x] + \sqrt{x - [x]}$
   (e) $f(x) = [x^2]$

4. Let $f$ be the function defined as follows on the interval $[0, 1]$: if $x = p/q$ is a rational number in its irreducible form, then $f(x) = (-1)^p q$; if $x$ is irrational, then $f(x) = 0$.

Show that $f$ has neither an upper bound nor a lower bound in any interval $[a, b]$, $0 \leqslant a < b \leqslant 1$.

# 7

# Limits of Functions

We hope that the notions developed in the preceding sections are now quite familiar, especially the concept of limit of a sequence of real numbers.

Now we shall study the notion of limit of a function at a point of its domain of definition.

Let $f$ be a real valued function, defined on a nonempty set $S$: assume that the real number $x_0$ is an accumulation point for the set $S$ (which implies automatically that the set $S$ has infinitely many elements: see page 35). Thus, given any natural number $M$, there exists at least one, and then infinitely many real numbers $x$ such that $0 < |x - x_0| < 1/M$. We stress that $x_0$ may or may not belong to $S$.

This assumption is verified in the most common cases: for example, when $f$ is defined at least on an interval $(a, b)$ and $a \leqslant x_0 \leqslant b$.

With these hypotheses, we define the function $f$.

The function $f$ has LIMIT $s$ AT THE POINT $x_0$ when, given $N$, an arbitrary natural number (as large as we like), there exists $M$, a natural number (depending on $N$), such that if $x$ is in $S$ and satisfies $0 < |x - x_0| < 1/M$ then $|f(x) - s| < 1/N$.

We write then $\lim_{x \to x_0} f(x) = s$.

Thus, if $s = \lim_{x \to x_0} f(x)$ then the values of the function $f$, at points of $S$ sufficiently near to $x_0$ but distinct from $x_0$, differ from $s$ by less than a given quantity, which may be as small as we like.

The illustration in Figure 7, corresponding to the case where $S = [a, b]$, $a < x_0 < b$, may be helpful.

Using this illustration, we can rephrase our definition of $s = \lim_{x \to x_0} f(x)$; it means that, given a horizontal strip around $s$ (as narrow as we like), it is possible to find a vertical strip around $x_0$, such that, the portion of the

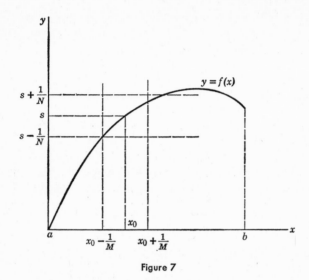

**Figure 7**

graph of the function inside the vertical strip is in the rectangle bounded by the horizontal strip, with the possible exception of the point $(x_0, f(x_0))$.

Moreover, in our drawing, we have $f(x_0) = \lim_{x \to x_0} f(x) = s$. However, as we shall see later, this is not always the case.

Another equivalent and very suggestive way of defining the notion of limit is as follows. We say that $s = \lim_{x \to x_0} f(x)$ when, given any neighborhood $U_N(s)$ of the point $s$ (as small as we like), there exists a neighborhood $U_M(x_0)$ of the point $x_0$ such that if $x \in U_M(x_0)$, $x \neq x_0$, and $f$ is defined at the point $x$, then $f(x) \in U_N(s)$. Thus, every neighborhood of $s$ contains the image by $f$ of some convenient neighborhood of $x_0$ (excluding, if necessary, the point $x_0$ itself). It is easy to verify the equivalence of this definition of limit with the preceding one, using the notion of neighborhood introduced in Chapter 5.

Another possible equivalent way of defining $\lim_{x \to x_0} f(x) = s$ is the following one. Given an arbitrary real number $\epsilon > 0$ (as small as we like), there exists a real number $\delta > 0$ (which depends on $\epsilon$), such that if $x$ is distinct from $x_0$, $x$ belongs to the interval $(x_0 - \delta, x_0 + \delta)$, and $f$ is defined at the point $x$, then $f(x)$ is in the interval $(s - \epsilon, s + \epsilon)$.

This definition is still equivalent to the preceding ones, since for every strictly positive real number $\epsilon$ (or $\delta$), there exists a sufficiently large integer $N$ such that $0 < 1/N < \epsilon$ (or $M$ such that $0 < 1/M < \delta$).

Note that, because of the condition contained in the definition of limit, we do not consider the value of $f(x)$ *at the point* $x_0$, but only at points sufficiently near to $x_0$. Therefore, it is allowable to speak of the limit of the function $f$ at the point $x_0$, even though $f$ is not defined at this point; however, we recall that $f$ is defined on a set $S$, for which $x_0$ is an accumulation point.

We now give some examples.

EXAMPLE 1. Let $f$ be the function defined on the real line and whose value in every point is equal to 1, that is, $f(x) = 1$ (constant function); then it is clear that in each point $x_0$ we have $\lim_{x \to x_0} f(x) = 1 = f(x_0)$.

EXAMPLE 2. Consider the function $f(x) = x^2$, defined on the set of all real numbers. We shall verify that in every point $x_0$ we have $f(x_0) = \lim_{x \to x_0} f(x)$, that is, $\lim_{x \to x_0} x^2 = x_0^2$. For this purpose, we must show that, given any natural number $N$, there exists a natural number $M$, such that if $0 < |x - x_0| < 1/M$ then $|x^2 - x_0^2| < 1/N$. We notice that

$$|x^2 - x_0^2| = |x - x_0| \cdot |x + x_0| = |x - x_0| \cdot |(x - x_0) + 2x_0|$$

$$\leq |x - x_0| \cdot (|x - x_0| + 2|x_0|) < \frac{1}{M}\left(\frac{1}{M} + 2|x_0|\right).$$

By choosing $M$ sufficiently large so that $(1/M).(1/M + 2|x_0|) < 1/N$, it follows from $|x - x_0| < 1/M$ that $|x^2 - x_0^2| < 1/N$.

Thus, it is enough to choose $M > N \cdot (1 + 2|x_0|)$, for this implies $(1/M).(1/M + 2|x_0|) < (1/M).(1 + 2|x_0|) < 1/N$.

Summarizing, given any natural number $N$, if we take a natural number $M$ as said, then $|x - x_0| < 1/M$ implies that $|x^2 - x_0^2| < 1/N$. This proves that $\lim_{x \to x_0} x^2 = x_0^2$ for every real number $x_0$.

We shall consider more examples after the following comments.

In our definition of limit of a function at a point $x_0$ we have required that $x_0$ be an accumulation point for the set $S$, on which the function $f$ is assumed to be defined; and we have taken into account the values of $f$ at all points in $S$, sufficiently close to $x_0$, distinct from $x_0$, and *on both sides of $x_0$.*

Sometimes, we want to describe separately the behavior of $f$ at each side of the point $x_0$.

Therefore, assume that $x_0$ is an accumulation point for the set $S_+$ of all elements $x$ in $S$, $x > x_0$. We say that $s_1$ is the RIGHT-HAND LIMIT of $f$ at the point $x_0$, when, given any natural number $N$, there exists a natural number $M$ (depending on $N$) such that if $x$ is in $S$, $0 < x - x_0 < 1/M$ then $|f(x) - s_1| < 1/N$. We use the notation $\lim_{x \to x_0+} f(x) = s_1$, where the sign $+$ indicates that the limit has been taken by considering only the values of $f$ in points near to $x_0$ and greater than $x_0$.

In similar way, if $x_0$ is an accumulation point for the set $S_-$ of all elements $x$ in $S$, $x < x_0$, we may define the LEFT-HAND LIMIT of $f$ at the point $x_0$. The task of stating this definition is an easy one, and we shall not undertake it here. The notation $\lim_{x \to x_0-} f(x) = s_2$ is now used, and its meaning is clear.

Of course, it may well happen that for a certain point $x_0$ both the right-hand and left-hand limits exist, but they are distinct. For example, let $f$ be the function defined as follows: $f(0) = 1/2$, $f(x) = 0$ when $x < 0$, $f(x) = 1$ when $x > 0$. At the point $x_0 = 0$ we have $\lim_{x \to x_0-} f(x) = 0$, $\lim_{x \to x_0+} f(x) = 1$.

It is quite easy to verify the following fact. Let $f$ be a function defined on a set $S$; let $x_0$ be an accumulation point, both for $S_+$ and $S_-$. If the right-hand and left-hand limits of $f$ at the point $x_0$ exist and are equal, then the limit of $f$ at $x_0$ exists and $\lim_{x \to x_0} f(x) = \lim_{x \to x_0+} f(x) = \lim_{x \to x_0-} f(x)$, and conversely, if $\lim_{x \to x_0} f(x)$ exists, then so do the one-sided limits, which are equal to the limit.

We still want to consider other cases in which it is interesting to define the notion of limit.

(1) Finite limit at the point $+\infty$.
(2) Infinite limit at a point $x_0$.
(3) Infinite limit at the point $+\infty$.
(4) Variants of the preceding cases, using $-\infty$.

Explicitly, we want to define the following limits.

$$\lim_{x \to +\infty} f(x) = s, \quad \lim_{x \to -\infty} f(x) = s$$

$$\lim_{x \to +\infty} f(x) = +\infty, \quad \lim_{x \to -\infty} f(x) = +\infty, \quad \lim_{x \to x_0} f(x) = +\infty$$

$$\lim_{x \to +\infty} f(x) = -\infty, \quad \lim_{x \to -\infty} f(x) = -\infty, \quad \lim_{x \to x_0} f(x) = -\infty$$

For example, if it is question of defining $\lim_{x \to +\infty} f(x)$, we have to assume that $f$ is defined for arbitrarily large values of $x$.

Using the language of neighborhoods, we have the advantage of providing one definition that is good for all the cases.

We recall that the neighborhoods of a real number have been introduced in Chapter 5. There we also defined the neighborhoods of $+\infty$, *in the set of natural numbers*. Here we shall need the neighborhoods of $+\infty$ and $-\infty$ *in the set of real numbers*.

We define an (*open*) *neighborhood* $U_N$ *of* $+\infty$ *in the set of real numbers*, as the set of all real numbers $x > N$. Similarly, we define an (open) neighborhood $U_{-N}$ of $-\infty$, as the set of real numbers $x < -N$.

In other words, neighborhoods of $+\infty$, $-\infty$, are nothing other than half-lines $(N, +\infty)$, $(-\infty, -N)$, where $N$ is any natural number.

Let $\alpha$, $\beta$ designate real numbers, or $+\infty$, or $-\infty$, and let us define $\lim_{x \to \alpha} f(x) = \beta$. This means that, given arbitrarily a neighborhood $U_N(\beta)$, as small as we like, it is possible to determine a neighborhood $U_M(\alpha)$ (which depends on $U_N(\beta)$) in such a way that if $x \in U_M(\alpha)$, $x \neq \alpha$ and $f$ is defined on $x$, then $f(x) \in U_N(\beta)$.

For example, if it is a question of the limit $\lim_{x \to +\infty} f(x) = s$, replacing $\alpha$ by $+\infty$ and $\beta$ by $s$, we obtain the following definition: given arbitrarily the neighborhood $U_N(s)$, it is possible to find a neighborhood $U_M(+\infty)$ such that if $x \in U_M(+\infty)$ (clearly $x \neq +\infty$) and $f$ is defined on $x$, then $f(x) \in U_N(s)$. If we want to avoid the wording of this definition by means of neighborhoods, we may translate it in more conventional language as follows: given any natural number $N$ (as large as we like), there exists a natural number $M$ (depending on $N$), such that if $x > M$, $x \in S$ then $|f(x) - s| < 1/N$.

It is worthwhile to recognize that if we take $S$ to be the set of all natural numbers, the function $f$ defined on $S$ is what we have called a sequence. The notion of $\lim_{x \to +\infty} f(x)$ reduces exactly to that of limit of a sequence.

As another example, consider the definition of $\lim_{x \to x_0} f(x) = -\infty$. It means that given any neighborhood $U_N(-\infty)$, there exists a neighborhood $U_M(x_0)$ such that if $x \in U_M(x_0)$, $x \in S$, and $x \neq x_0$ then $f(x) \in U_N(-\infty)$. Without referring to neighborhoods, we rephrase as follows: given any natural number $N$ (as large as we like), there exists a natural number $M$ (depending on $N$) such that if $x \in S$, $0 < |x - x_0| < 1/M$ then $f(x) < -N$.

The other definitions may be stated as an exercise.

The following examples with infinite limits, will be treated quite informally; later, after studying the properties of limits on pp. 79–83, an attempt should be made to justify all the steps.

EXAMPLE 1. Consider the function $f(x) = 1/x^2$, whose domain of definition is the set of all real numbers $x \neq 0$; then $\lim_{x \to 0} f(x) = +\infty$ (see Figure 8).

Indeed, we must show that $\lim_{x \to 0+} f(x) = +\infty$ and also that $\lim_{x \to 0-} f(x) = +\infty$. Calling $1/x = t$, if $x$ tends to 0, at the right, then $t = 1/x$ tends to $+\infty$. Therefore, to show that $\lim_{x \to 0+} f(x) = +\infty$ is equivalent to showing that $\lim_{t \to +\infty} t^2 = +\infty$, and this is clearly true. Similarly, to show that

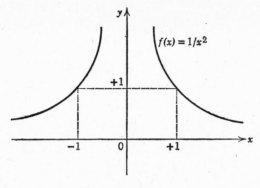

**Figure 8**

$\lim\limits_{x\to 0-} f(x) = +\infty$ is the same as proving that $\lim\limits_{t\to -\infty} t^2 = +\infty$, and this is also true.

An inspection of the graph (Figure 8) of the function $f(x) = 1/x^2$ leads us to the same conclusion.

EXAMPLE 2. Consider the functions $f(x) = x$ and $g(x) = -x$. It is clear that $\lim\limits_{x\to +\infty} f(x) = +\infty$, $\lim\limits_{x\to -\infty} f(x) = -\infty$, $\lim\limits_{x\to +\infty} g(x) = -\infty$, $\lim\limits_{x\to -\infty} g(x) = +\infty$.

EXAMPLE 3. If $f(x) = \dfrac{x+1}{x}$, then $\lim\limits_{x\to +\infty} f(x) = 1$ and $\lim\limits_{x\to -\infty} f(x) = 1$.

EXAMPLE 4. The function $y = \tan x$ does not have limit at the point $x_0 = \pi/2$ because $\lim\limits_{x\to x_0+} \tan x = -\infty$, while $\lim\limits_{x\to x_0-} \tan x = +\infty$. We may convince ourselves of these facts by examining the graph of this function (Figure 9). Actually, for all the points of the form $n.\pi + \pi/2$ (where $n$ is an integer) we have the same behavior.

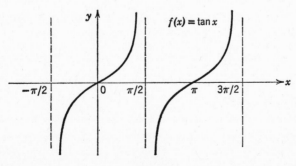

**Figure 9**

Now we shall derive a proposition on limits of functions, similar to the ones already proved for limits of sequences.

*Uniqueness of the Limit.    If* $\lim_{x \to \alpha} f(x)$ *exists, it is unique.*

In fact, let us assume that $\beta = \lim_{x \to \alpha} f(x)$ and also $\beta' = \lim_{x \to \alpha} f(x)$, with $\beta \neq \beta'$.

If $\beta$, $\beta'$ are both finite (for example, if $\beta < \beta'$), it is clearly possible to find a natural number $N$ so large that $\beta + 1/N < \beta' - 1/N$. For this value of $N$, there exists a neighborhood $U_M(\alpha)$ such that if $x \in U_M(\alpha)$, $x \neq \alpha$ and $f$ is defined on $x$, then $|f(x) - \beta| < 1/N$ because $\lim_{x \to \alpha} f(x) = \beta$. Similarly, for this value of $N$, there exists a neighborhood $U_{M'}(\alpha)$ such that if $x \in U_{M'}(\alpha)$, $x \neq \alpha$ and $f$ is defined on $x$, then $|f(x) - \beta'| < 1/N$. If we take the smallest of these two neighborhoods of $\alpha$ (which corresponds to the largest of the numbers $M$, $M'$), it is clear that for this neighborhood both conditions are satisfied, that is, $|f(x) - \beta| < 1/N$ and $|f(x) - \beta'| < 1/N$; hence $f(x) < \beta + 1/N$, $\beta' - 1/N < f(x)$. But this is impossible, since $\beta + 1/N < \beta' - 1/N$. Therefore, we must have $\beta = \beta'$.

The same argument may be applied to the cases where $\beta$ is finite, $\beta'$ is $+\infty$ or $-\infty$, or vice versa. Thus, in any case, the limit, whenever it exists, must be unique.

### Relations Between Limit of a Function and Limit of Sequences

In the definition of the limit of a function, no mention has been made of any sequence. Intuitively, however, our idea that $\lim_{x \to \alpha} f(x) = \beta$ (real number) is the following one. When $x$ is approaching $\alpha$, by closer and closer numbers $x_1, x_2, \ldots, x_n, \ldots$ (distinct from $\alpha$), then the values of the function $f$, namely, $f(x_1), f(x_2), f(x_3), \ldots, f(x_n), \ldots$, are getting nearer to $\beta$. Consequently, somehow, there is a relation between the limit of a function at $\alpha$ and the limit of a sequence of values of this function.

Precisely, we have the following result.

*In order that* $\lim_{x \to \alpha} f(x) = \beta$ *(where $\beta$ is a real number, or $+\infty$, or $-\infty$) it is necessary and sufficient that for every sequence $(x_n)$, with every $x_n \in S$, $x_n \neq \alpha$, and* $\lim x_n = \alpha$, *we have* $\lim f(x_n) = \beta$.

We shall give proof only for the case where $\beta$ is finite, suggesting that proof of the other cases be done as an exercise. We notice that, since $\alpha$ is an accumulation point for $S$, there exist sequences $(x_n)$ of elements of $S$, $x_n \neq \alpha$, such that $\lim x_n = \alpha$.

First we assume that $\lim\limits_{x\to\alpha} f(x) = \beta$, and we consider any one sequence $(x_n)$, such that every $x_n \neq \alpha$, $x_n \in S$ and $\lim x_n = \alpha$. We want to show that $\lim f(x_n) = \beta$.

In fact, given any natural number $N$, there exists an integer $M > 0$ such that if $0 < |x - \alpha| < 1/M$, $x \in S$, then $|f(x) - \beta| < 1/N$.

Since $\lim x_n = \alpha$, for the above integer $M$, there exists an index $n_0$ such that if $n \geqslant n_0$ then $|x_n - \alpha| < 1/M$; therefore, $|f(x_n) - \beta| < 1/N$ for every index $n \geqslant n_0$. This means that $\lim f(x_n) = \beta$.

Now we prove the converse. If it were not true (that is, $\lim\limits_{x\to\alpha} f(x) = \beta$ is false), there would exist a natural number $N$ with the following property: for every index $n$ there exists some real number $x_n$ such that $0 < |x_n - \alpha| < 1/n$, $x_n \in S$; however, $|f(x_n) - \beta| > 1/N$. We have thus obtained a sequence $(x_n)$, all of whose terms are in $S$, different from $\alpha$, and $\lim x_n = \alpha$; indeed, for every natural number $n$, taking $n_0 = n$, we deduce that for every index $m \geqslant n_0$ we have $|x_m - \alpha| < 1/m \leqslant 1/n$. However, from the assumption made, we have $\lim f(x_n) \neq \beta$, and this is a contradiction!

The advantage of this result is that it enables us to make use of our knowledge about limits of sequences.

## Operations with Limits of Functions

Let $f$ and $g$ be functions defined on a set $S$; let $\alpha$ be a real number which is an accumulation point for the set $S$, or let $\alpha = +\infty$, and then assume that the set $S$ has arbitrarily large real numbers.*

*If* $\lim\limits_{x\to\alpha} f(x) = \beta$ *and* $\lim\limits_{x\to\alpha} g(x) = \gamma$ *(where* $\beta$, $\gamma$ *are real numbers or* $+\infty$, *or* $-\infty$*), then, under the restrictions mentioned below, the following equalities hold.*

(1) $\lim\limits_{x\to\alpha} (f(x) + g(x)) = \beta + \gamma$

(2) $\lim\limits_{x\to\alpha} (f(x) - g(x)) = \beta - \gamma$

(3) $\lim\limits_{x\to\alpha} (f(x).g(x)) = \beta.\gamma$

(4) $\lim\limits_{x\to\alpha} (f(x)/g(x)) = \beta/\gamma$

*Restrictions.* It is necessary that the operations indicated on the right-hand sides, above, make sense. For example, if $\beta = +\infty$, $\gamma = -\infty$, then the right-hand side of (1) does not have any meaning, since we did not define

---

* We might also say that $\alpha = +\infty$ is an accumulation point for $S$ since, in every neighborhood of $\alpha$, there exist points of $S$.

$(+\infty) + (-\infty)$; thus, in this case (1) is not valid. Generally speaking, the equalities hold true, provided that on the right-hand side no expression of the types $(+\infty) + (-\infty)$, $(+\infty) - (+\infty)$, $(-\infty) + (+\infty)$, $(-\infty) - (-\infty)$, $0.(+\infty)$, $0.(-\infty)$, $0/0$, $\pm\infty/\pm\infty$, $\pm\infty/0$, $\beta/0$ appear. For this last case, we must take special care since, in general, it is not possible to conclude that the function $f/g$ possesses at the point $\alpha$ an infinite limit. It may happen that the above quotient has a left-hand limit $-\infty$ and a right-hand limit $+\infty$, as in the case where $f(x) = 1$, $g(x) = x$ and $\alpha = 0$. It may even happen that the function $f/g$ does not have a left-hand limit or right-hand limit; for example, $f(x) = 1$, $g(x) = x \cdot \sin 1/x$, at the point $\alpha = 0$ (as an exercise, verify that $\lim\limits_{x\to 0} x \cdot \sin 1/x = 0$; however, the function $(1/x) \cdot \sin \dfrac{1}{x}$ has no one-sided limits at the point 0; cf. Exercise 1 on page 84).

If $\beta$, $\gamma$ are *finite*, then the equalities (1), (2), (3) hold. If $\beta$, $\gamma$ are finite and $\gamma \neq 0$, then (4) holds.

In the proof of these equalities, we shall restrict ourselves to the case where $\beta$, $\gamma$ are finite, suggesting that the other cases be proved as exercises.

We shall use the corresponding results for limits of sequences, as well as the preceding property. As an example, we shall prove (1).

We have $\lim\limits_{x\to\alpha} f(x) = \beta$, respectively $\lim\limits_{x\to\alpha} g(x) = \gamma$, if and only if for every sequence $(x_n)$, with every $x_n \in S$, $x_n \neq \alpha$, and $\lim x_n = \alpha$, it is true that $\lim f(x_n) = \beta$, respectively $\lim g(x_n) = \gamma$.

From the properties for limits of sequences, it follows that

$$\lim (f(x_n) + g(x_n)) = \beta + \gamma;$$

this being true for every sequence $(x_n)$, as before, by the preceding property, we deduce that $\lim\limits_{x\to\alpha} (f(x) + g(x)) = \beta + \gamma$.

### Conservation of Inequalities by Passing to the Limit

*Let $f$, $g$ be functions defined on a set $S$, for which $x_0$ is an accumulation point. Assume that there exists some neighborhood of $x_0$ such that for every point $x \in S$, $x \neq x_0$ in this neighborhood we have $f(x) \leqslant g(x)$. Moreover, we assume that the limits $\lim\limits_{x\to x_0} f(x)$, $\lim\limits_{x\to x_0} g(x)$ exist (being possibly infinite). Then $\lim\limits_{x\to x_0} f(x) \leqslant \lim\limits_{x\to x_0} g(x)$.*

In a more suggestive language, we may state that inequalities are preserved by passing to the limit.

Indeed, if $\lim\limits_{x\to x_0} f(x) = \beta$, $\lim\limits_{x\to x_0} g(x) = \gamma$ and $\beta > \gamma$ (where $\beta$, $\gamma$ are real numbers, or $+\infty$, or $-\infty$), there exists a natural number $N$, so large that $U_N(\beta)$, $U_N(\gamma)$ have no point in common (for example, if $\beta$, $\gamma$ are finite we need only to take $N > 2/(\beta - \gamma)$; if $\beta = +\infty$, $\gamma$ is finite, we take $N > \gamma + 1$, and so on). With this choice of $N$, all the numbers in $U_N(\gamma)$ are strictly smaller than those of $U_N(\beta)$. Associated with this integer $N$, there exists a natural number $M_1$ such that if $x \in S$, $x \neq x_0$, $x \in U_{M_1}(x_0)$ then $f(x) \in U_N(\beta)$. In the same way, there exists a natural number $M_2$ such that if $x \in S$, $x \neq x_0$, $x \in U_{M_2}(x_0)$ then $g(x) \in U_N(\gamma)$. Taking $M$ to be the largest of the numbers $M_1$, $M_2$, and $x \in S$, $x \neq x_0$, $x \in U_M(x_0)$, it follows that $f(x) \in U_N(\beta)$, $g(x) \in U_N(\gamma)$. Therefore $f(x) > g(x)$ for every $x \in U_M(x_0)$, $x \in S$, $x \neq x_0$. However, this contradicts the hypothesis of existence of a neighborhood of $x_0$ on which $f(x) \leqslant g(x)$, for every $x \in$ $x \neq x_0$. From this contradiction, we deduce that $\beta \leqslant \gamma$.

We state without proof some variants of this proposition.

(1) If $f$, $g$ are functions defined on a set $S$ containing arbitrarily large real numbers, and if there exists a neighborhood of $+\infty$ where $f(x) \leqslant g(x)$, then (in case the limits $\lim_{x \to +\infty} f(x)$, $\lim_{x \to +\infty} g(x)$ exist) we must have $\lim_{x \to +\infty} f(x) \leqslant$ $\lim_{x \to +\infty} g(x)$.

A similar statement may be made concerning $-\infty$.

(2) This is a particular case. If $f(x) \leqslant a$ (real number) for every $x \in S$, in some neighborhood of $\alpha$ (with exclusion of a), where $\alpha$ is a real number or $+\infty$, or $-\infty$, and if $\lim_{x \to \alpha} f(x)$ exists, then $\lim_{x \to \alpha} f(x) \leqslant a$.

A corresponding statement holds true when $f(x) \geqslant a$.

(3) The analogous statements for right-hand and left-hand limits are still valid, provided the hypotheses are correctly stated.

A comment, similar to the one made for sequences, is now in order. If $f(x) < g(x)$ for every number $x \in S$ in a neighborhood of $\alpha$, $x \neq \alpha$, we cannot in general conclude that (when the limits in question exist) $\lim_{x \to \alpha} f(x) < \lim_{x \to \alpha} g(x)$. All we can say is that $\lim_{x \to \alpha} f(x) \leqslant \lim_{x \to \alpha} g(x)$. The same applies for one-sided limits.

For example, let $g(x) = |x|$, $f(x) = 0$ (constant function) and $\alpha = 0$. Then $0 < |x|$ when $x \neq 0$, however $0 = \lim_{x \to 0} |x|$.

We conclude this chapter by giving some important examples of limits of functions.

EXAMPLE 1.* $\lim_{x \to 0} \sin x/x = 1$.

---

\* As we warned on page 66, we are using trigonometric functions freely as examples, granting that a complete justification of their definitions and properties may be achieved by means of the theory of power series.

We know that considering a circle (Figure 10) with radius equal to 1, if $x$ is the measure in radians of the arc $AC$ then $\overline{SC} = \sin x$, $\overline{AT} = \tan x$, and we have the following inequalities: $0 < \sin x < x < \tan x$ (valid when $0 < x < \pi/2$).

Dividing each term by the positive number $\sin x$, we obtain

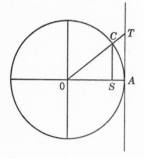

Figure 10

$$1 < \frac{x}{\sin x} < \frac{\tan x}{\sin x} = \frac{1}{\cos x}$$

Since

$$\lim_{x \to 0} \cos x = 1 = \cos 0$$

it follows from proposition (4) on page 79 that

$$\lim_{x \to 0} \frac{1}{\cos x} = 1.$$

Using the proposition on the conservation of inequalities at the limit, we deduce that

$$1 \leqslant \lim_{x \to 0+} \frac{x}{\sin x} \leqslant \lim_{x \to 0+} \frac{1}{\cos x} = 1.$$

hence

$$\lim_{x \to 0+} \frac{x}{\sin x} = 1.$$

In the same way we may verify, with a little care on the signs of the arcs, sines, and tangents, that

$$\lim_{x \to 0-} \frac{x}{\sin x} = 1.$$

We conclude, therefore that,

$$\lim_{x \to 0} \frac{x}{\sin x} = 1.$$

Some consequences are the following ones.

(a) $\lim\limits_{x \to 0} \dfrac{1 - \cos x}{x} = 0.$

In fact,

$$\frac{1 - \cos x}{x} = \frac{(1 - \cos x) \cdot (1 + \cos x)}{x \cdot (1 + \cos x)} = \frac{1 - \cos^2 x}{x \cdot (1 + \cos x)}$$

$$= \frac{\sin^2 x}{x \cdot (1 + \cos x)} = \frac{\sin x}{x} \cdot \frac{1}{1 + \cos x} \cdot \sin x.$$

Hence

$$\lim_{x\to 0}\frac{1-\cos x}{x} = \lim_{x\to 0}\frac{\sin x}{x}\cdot\lim_{x\to 0}\frac{1}{1+\cos x}\cdot\lim_{x\to 0}\sin x = 0$$

since

$$\lim_{x\to 0}\frac{\sin x}{x} = 1/\left(\lim_{x\to 0}\frac{x}{\sin x}\right) = 1,$$

and

$$\lim_{x\to 0}\frac{1}{1+\cos x} = \frac{1}{2}, \quad \lim_{x\to 0}\sin x = 0.$$

(b) $\displaystyle\lim_{x\to 0}\frac{\tan x}{x} = 1$.

In fact,

$$\lim_{x\to 0}\frac{\tan x}{x} = \lim_{x\to 0}\frac{\sin x}{x\cdot\cos x} = \lim_{x\to 0}\frac{1}{\cos x}\cdot\lim_{x\to 0}\frac{\sin x}{x} = 1.$$

EXAMPLE 2. Determination of

$$\lim_{x\to+\infty}\frac{a_0 x^n + a_1 x^{n-1} + \ldots + a_n}{b_0 x^m + b_1 x^{m-1} + \ldots + b_m}$$

where $a_0, b_0 > 0$.

We first assume that $n > m$. Dividing the numerator and the denominator of the above rational function by $x^m$, we obtain

$$r(x) = \frac{a_0 x^n + a_1 x^{n-1} + \ldots + a_n}{b_0 x^m + b_1 x^{m-1} + \ldots + b^m} = \frac{a_0 x^{n-m} + \ldots + a_{n-1} x^{-m+1} + a_n x^{-m}}{b_0 + b_1 x^{-1} + \ldots + b_m x^{-m}}$$

Hence,

$$\lim_{x\to+\infty} r(x) = \frac{\text{limit of the numerator}}{\text{limit of the denominator}} = \frac{+\infty}{b_0} = +\infty.$$

We now consider the case where $n = m$. The same process gives $\lim_{x\to+\infty} r(x) = a_0/b_0$.

Finally, we assume that $n < m$. Again we obtain

$$\lim_{x\to+\infty} r(x) = \lim_{x\to+\infty}\frac{a_0 + a_1 x^{-1} + \ldots + a_{n-1} x^{-n+1} + a_n x^{-n}}{b_0 x^{m-n} + b_1 x^{m-n-1} + \ldots + b_m x^{-n}} = \frac{a_0}{+\infty} = 0.$$

Notice that the above manipulations are based on our results on operations with limits (page 79). We recall that we did not exclude the possibility that some of the limits might be $+\infty$ or $=\infty$, as soon as the expressions written made sense; for example, $+\infty/b_0 = +\infty$, $a_0/+\infty = 0$ when $b_0 > 0$, $a_0$ is real.

**Exercises**

1. For each of the functions in Exercises 1 and 3 on pp. 70 and 71, describe the points presenting special particularities; that is, the points listed below.

(a) Points where the function is not defined.

(b) Points where the right-hand limit or the left-hand limit do not exist.

(c) Points where the right-hand and left-hand limit exist but are distinct.

(d) Points where the function has some of the right-hand or left-hand limit infinity.

2. For each of the functions of Exercises 1 and 3 (above-mentioned), determine (when it makes sense) the limit of the function when $x$ tends to $+\infty$.

3. Determine the following limits, in the event that they exist.

(a) $\lim\limits_{x \to 1} \dfrac{x^7 - 2x^5 + 1}{x^3 - 3x^2 + 2}$

(b) $\lim\limits_{x \to 2} \dfrac{x^8 - 2^8}{x - 2}$

(c) $\lim\limits_{x \to 0} \dfrac{\sqrt{1 + x + x^2} - 1}{x}$

(d) $\lim\limits_{x \to 0} \dfrac{\sqrt{1 + x} - 1}{x}$

(e) $\lim\limits_{x \to +\infty} \sqrt{\dfrac{x + 1}{2}} \, [\sqrt{x + 1} - \sqrt{x}]$

(f) $\lim\limits_{x \to 0} \left[ \dfrac{\sin 2x}{x} + \dfrac{x}{\sin 2x} + \dfrac{1 - x}{1 + x} \right]$

(g) $\lim\limits_{x \to 1} \dfrac{\sqrt{1 + x} - \sqrt{1 + x^2}}{\sqrt{1 - x^2} - \sqrt{1 - x}}$

(h) $\lim\limits_{x \to 1} \dfrac{1 + \cos \pi x}{\tan^2 \pi x}$

(i) $\lim\limits_{x \to \pi/2} (\sec x - \tan x)$

(j) $\lim\limits_{x \to 0} \dfrac{\sqrt{1 + x} - \sqrt{1 - x}}{x}$

4. Show that

$$\lim_{x \to 0} \frac{x + 3}{x + 5} = \frac{3}{5},$$

verifying directly in the definition of limit that, given any integer $N$ (for example, $N = 10$, $N = 100$, $N = 1000$), it is possible to find a natural integer $M$ such that if $|x| < 1/M$ then

$$\left| \frac{x + 3}{x + 5} - \frac{3}{5} \right| < \frac{1}{N}$$

# 8

# Continuous Functions

We shall now study the type of functions most commonly found in practice and which corresponds to the great majority of physical phenomena. They are the continuous functions.

Let $f$ be a function defined on a set $S$; let $x_0$ be a point of $S$ which is an accumulation point for $S$; thus, it is possible to consider the value $f(x_0)$ as well as the notion of limit of $f$ at $x_0$.

With this hypothesis, we say that $f$ is CONTINUOUS AT THE POINT $x_0$ whenever $\lim_{x \to x_0} f(x)$ exists and is equal to $f(x_0)$.

For convenience, we shall also agree that if $x_0$ is an ISOLATED POINT of $S$ (that is, a point which is *not* an accumulation point for $S$), then $f$ is continuous at $x_0$. This agreement does not contradict the preceding definition, since the $\lim_{x \to x_0} f(x)$ does not exist whenever $x_0$ is not an accumulation point for $S$.

Since $x_0$ is in the domain of definition of $f$, then $f(x_0)$ is a real number, and is thus neither $+\infty$, nor $-\infty$. Therefore, $\lim_{x \to x_0} f(x)$ is finite. Consequently, if it is known that $f$ has an infinite limit at the point $x_0$, it cannot be continuous at this point.

The definition of continuity of a function $f$ at a point $x_0$ may be reformulated as follows. Given any natural number $N$ (as large as we like), there exists a natural number $M$ (which depends on $N$) such that if $|x - x_0| < 1/M$ and $x$ is in the domain of definition of $f$, then

$$|f(x) - f(x_0)| < 1/N.$$

This definition is simply obtained from the definition of limit by replacing the number $s$ by $f(x_0)$. We do not require here that $x \neq x_0$, since we know *a priori* that $f$ is defined for $x = x_0$ and, at this point, $f(x) - f(x_0) = 0$.

We notice also that if $x_0$ is an isolated point of $S$, then the above condition is automatically verified for $x_0$: it is sufficient to take $M$ so large that no point $x$ of $S$, $x \neq x_0$, exists such that $|x - x_0| < 1/M$.

It follows from the result on page 78 that the continuity of a function $f$ at a point $x_0$ may be expressed in the following equivalent way.

*If $(x_n)$ is any sequence of points in the domain of definition of $f$ such that $\lim_{n \to \infty} x_n = x_0$, then $(f(x_n))$ is also a convergent sequence and $\lim_{n \to \infty} f(x_n) = f(x_0)$.*

We may also write this property as $\lim_{n \to \infty} f(x_n) = f(\lim_{n \to \infty} x_n)$ and say that *the continuous function $f$ "commutes" with the limiting process.*

Now that we have introduced the notion of a function continuous at a point $x_0$, we shall define a CONTINUOUS FUNCTION ON A SET, contained in the domain of definition of the function.

Thus, let $f$ be a function and let $S'$ be a set contained in the domain of definition $S$ of the function $f$. We say that $f$ *is continuous on $S'$* whenever it is continuous at every point $x_0$ of $S'$.

We say that the function $f$ is CONTINUOUS (without specifying where), whenever $f$ is continuous at *every* point of its domain of definition.

## Examples of Continuous Functions

The class of continuous functions is very large. Every constant function $f(x) = a$ is a continuous function. Every function of the type $f(x) = ax^n$, where $a$ is a real number and $n$ a natural integer, is also a continuous function.

*The sum or difference of a finite number of continuous functions is again a continuous function*, at every point $x_0$ in the domains of definition of the given functions.

To verify this fact, it is clearly sufficient to consider two functions and to apply the proposition stated on page 79, with $\beta = f(x_0)$, $\gamma = g(x_0)$. Thus, $\lim_{x \to x_0} (f(x) \pm g(x)) = f(x_0) \pm g(x_0)$.

*The product of a finite number of continuous functions is a continuous function*, at every point $x_0$ in the domains of definition of the given functions.

This may be seen in similar way.

As a consequence, we conclude that every polynomial function $f(x) = x^n + a_1 x^{n-1} + \ldots + a_{n-1} x + a_n$, with real coefficients, is a continuous function (on the whole real line).

*If the functions $f$, $g$ are continuous at the point $x_0$ and if $g(x_0) \neq 0$, then the function $f/g$ is continuous at $x_0$* because we may apply the proposition given on page 79.

It follows that a rational function

$$r(x) = \frac{f(x)}{g(x)} = \frac{a_0 x^n + a_1 x^{n-1} + \ldots + a_{n-1} x + a_n}{b_0 x^m + b_1 x^{m-1} + \ldots + b_{m-1} x + b_m}$$

is continuous at every point $x_0$ such that $g(x_0) \neq 0$. Since there exists, at most, a finite number of values $x$ for which $g(x) = 0$ (these are the roots of the polynomial $g$), then the rational function $r$ is continuous at every point of the real line, with a finite number of exceptions.

Many other continuous functions exist. For example, the functions sine and cosine are continuous. The function tangent is continuous at every point, except those such as $n.\pi + \pi/2$, where $n$ is any integer.

We may increase the number of examples of continuous functions, using the following two propositions. The first asserts the continuity of a function of a function, while the second refers to the continuity of the inverse function.

PROPOSITION. *Every continuous function of a continuous function of x is a continuous function of x.* Precisely, let $y = f(x)$ be a continuous function defined on the set $S$; let $z = g(y)$ be a continuous function defined on the set $T$, which contains the range of the function $f$. Then $z = g(f(x)) = (g \circ f)(x)$ is a continuous function of $x$.

To prove the proposition, let $x_0$ be any point of the set $S$, and $y_0 = f(x_0)$, $z_0 = g(y_0)$. Since the function $g$ is continuous at the point $y_0$, given any natural number $N$, there exists a natural number $L$, such that if $y$ is in the domain of definition of $g$ and $|y - y_0| < 1/L$ then $|g(y) - g(y_0)| < 1/N$. In the same way, since $f$ is continuous at the point $x_0$, associated with the above number $L$, there exists a natural number $M$ such that if $x$ is in the domain of definition of $f$ and $|x - x_0| < 1/M$ then $|f(x) - y_0| < 1/L$.

Now we shall combine these facts. To the arbitrary natural number $N$ we associate the number $M$; if $x$ is in the set $S$ and $|x - x_0| < 1/M$ then, by hypothesis, $f(x)$ is in the set $T$, domain of definition of $g$, and therefore, $|g(f(x)) - g(y_0)| < 1/N$, that is, $|(g \circ f)(x) - (g \circ f)(x_0)| < 1/N$.

This shows the continuity of $g \circ f$ at the point $x_0$. Since $x_0$ was an arbitrary point of the set $S$, it follows that $g \circ f$ is continuous.

As an application of this result, we conclude from the continuity of the functions $y = x^2$ and $z = \sin y$ that $z = \sin x^2$ is also a continuous function. Similarly, we know that $y = \tan x$ is continuous except for the points of type $n.\pi + \pi/2$, and $z = (y + 1)/(y - 1)$ is continuous except for $y = 1$; it follows that the function $z = (\tan x + 1)/(\tan x - 1)$ is surely continuous at the interval $(-1, +1)$.

Before considering the continuity of the inverse function of a continuous function, we shall establish some properties of continuous functions, which will be needed in the proof. Actually, these properties are important in their own light. They serve to describe the behavior of any one continuous function, making more precise the intuitive idea expressed in the definition of continuity.

Thus, logically, the propositions that follow may be grouped into two types: (1) those describing the behavior of each continuous function and (2) those referring to the class of all continuous functions, and disclosing, without direct use of the definition, which functions may be easily recognized as continuous.

PROPOSITION. *Let $f$ be a function continuous on the set $S$ and let $x_0$ be a point in this set. If $f(x_0) > 0$ then there exists a natural number $M$ such that if $x \in S$ and $|x - x_0| < 1/M$ then $f(x) > 0$. In the same way, if $f(x_0) < 0$ then, in some sufficiently small interval around $x_0$ the values of the function at every $x \in S$ are all negative.*

We prove the first assertion, the other being similar.

Since $f$ is continuous at the point $x_0$, given any natural number $N$, there exists a natural number $M$ such that if $x$ is in $S$ and $|x - x_0| < 1/M$ then $|f(x) - f(x_0)| < 1/N$.

In particular, we may choose $N$ such that $N > 2/f(x_0)$, hence $1/N < f(x_0)/2$. With this choice of $N$, we obtain $|f(x) - f(x_0)| < 1/N < f(x_0)/2$. This implies that $f(x) > 0$ for every $x$ in $S$ such that $|x - x_0| < 1/M$.

In fact, if for some of these values of $x$ we would have $f(x) \leqslant 0$ then
$$f(x_0) = |f(x_0)| = |f(x) + (f(x_0) - f(x))|$$
$$\leqslant |f(x)| + |f(x_0) - f(x)| \leqslant |f(x_0) - f(x)| < 1/2f(x_0),$$
and this is impossible. Thus, we have indeed $f(x) > 0$ for every such $x$.

COROLLARY. *Let $f$ be a function defined on the set $S$ and continuous at the point $x_0$ of $S$.*

    (a) *If, for every natural number $N$ (as large as we like), there exists some $x$ in $S$ for which $|x - x_0| < 1/N$, and $f(x) = 0$, then necessarily $f(x_0) = 0$.*

    (b) *If, for every natural number $N$ (as large as we like), there exists some $x_1$ and $x_2$ in $S$, such that $|x_1 - x_0| < 1/N$ and $|x_2 - x_0| < 1/N$, for which $f(x_1) < 0$ and $f(x_2) > 0$, then necessarily $f(x_0) = 0$.*

This corollary follows easily from the proposition. If it were $f(x_0) > 0$ (or $f(x_0) < 0$), there would exist a sufficiently small interval around $x_0$, that is, there would exist a natural number $N$, sufficiently large, such that for every $x \in S$ in the interval $(x_0 - 1/N, x_0 + 1/N)$ we would have $f(x) > 0$ (or correspondingly $f(x) < 0$). This is against the hypotheses (a) and (b).

## Intermediate-Value Property of Continuous Functions

    (1) *Let $f$ be a continuous function on an interval $I$, let $a$, $b$ be points of $I$, $a < b$, and let us assume that $f(a) < 0$, $f(b) > 0$ (or similarly $f(a) > 0, f(b) < 0$). Then, there exists a point $x_0$ in the interval $(a, b)$, such that $f(x_0) = 0$. In other*

words, in order to pass from a negative value to a positive value (or vice versa), a continuous function must assume some value zero.

(2) *Let f be a continuous function on an interval I, let a, b be points of I, a < b, and let $f(a) = \alpha$, $f(b) = \beta$. If $y_0$ is any intermediate value, that is, $\alpha < y_0 < \beta$ (or, similarly, $\beta < y_0 < \alpha$), then there exists a point $x_0$ in $(a, b)$ such that $f(x_0) = y_0$.* In a more suggestive way, we may also say that a continuous function assumes in $[a, b]$ all the values between $f(a), f(b)$.

To prove this proposition, we first note that part (1) is a special case of part (2), obtained by letting $\alpha < 0, \beta > 0$ and $y_0 = 0$. However, we find it simpler to prove part (1) and deduce part (2) as an easy consequence.

*Proof of part (1).* Consider the set $T$ formed by all the points $x$ in the interval $[a, b]$ such that if $x'$ is in $[a, b]$ and $x' \leqslant x$, then $f(x') \leqslant 0$. For example, the point $a$ has this property; however, $b$ does not belong to the set $T$, since $f(b) > 0$. Clearly, if $x$ is in the set $T$ then every point of $[a, b]$ to the left of $x$ is still in $T$.

The set $T$, so defined, is contained in $[a, b]$, thus it is bounded above. By the theorem on page 58, $T$ has a least upper bound, which we denote by $x_0$. We now show that $f(x_0) = 0$.

In fact, if it were $f(x_0) \neq 0$, by the proposition on page 89 there would exist a sufficiently small neighborhood $(x_0 - 1/N, x_0 + 1/N)$ of $x_0$ such that, for every $x$ in this neighborhood, $f(x)$ and $f(x_0)$ have the same sign; both are positive, or both are negative.

If $f(x_0) < 0$ and $x_1$ is such that $x_0 < x_1 < x_0 + 1/N$, then $f(x) < 0$ for every $x < x_1$; hence, $x_1$ belongs to the set $T$, but it is strictly greater than the least upper bound $x_0$ of $T$. This is impossible.

If, on the other hand, $f(x_0) > 0$, then for every $x_1$ such that $x_0 - 1/N < x_1 < x_0$ we have $f(x_1) > 0$. Therefore no such point $x_1$ is in the set $T$; it follows that the least upper bound $x_0$ of $T$ is not greater than $x_0 - 1/N$. This, however, is a contradiction.

Thus, the only possibility is that $f(x_0) = 0$.

*Proof of part (2).* Assume, for example, that $\alpha < y_0 < \beta$ (the other case being analogous). We define the function $g$ as follows: $g(x) = f(x) - y_0$ for every $x$ in the interval. In particular, $g(a) = f(a) - y_0 = \alpha - y_0 < 0$, $g(b) = f(b) - y_0 = \beta - y_0 > 0$. Clearly, $g$ is a continuous function. Since it satisfies the hypothesis of part (1), there exists a point $x_0$ in $(a, b)$ such that $g(x_0) = 0$; in other words, $f(x_0) = y_0$.

This fundamental theorem may also be interpreted in the following sense: *a continuous function does not have any "jump" in its graph* and, thus, it conforms to the intuitive meaning of continuity. We may draw the graph of a continuous function on an interval $[a, b]$, starting from the value $f(a)$ and reaching the value $f(b)$, without taking the pencil off the paper. This is the way certain instruments register the measure of physical quantities (such as barographs, thermographs, and so on); they trace a graph describing the continuous variation of these quantities, without jumping from one value to another.

WEIERSTRASS'S THEOREM ON THE MAXIMUM AND MINIMUM ATTAINED ON CLOSED INTERVALS. *Let f be a function, continuous on a closed interval* $[a, b]$. *Then we have:*

(1) *The range of values of f is a bounded set; therefore it has a least upper bound U and a greatest lower bound L.*

(2) *There exists at least a point* $x'$ *in* $[a, b]$ *for which* $f(x') = U$ *and at least a point* $x''$ *in* $[a, b]$ *for which* $f(x'') = L$.

Therefore, on a closed interval a continuous function cannot increase or decrease indefinitely; on the contrary, it assumes a maximum and a minimum value.

*Proof (for the case of least upper bound).* We first prove that the range of values of $f$ is a bounded set. If this were not true, then for every natural number $n$ there would exist an element, which we call $x_n$, in the interval $[a, b]$ such that $|f(x_n)| > n$. In this way, we obtain a sequence $(x_n)$, which is bounded, since always $a \leqslant x_n \leqslant b$.

By the proposition on page 47, it is possible to select a convergent subsequence $x_{n_1}, x_{n_2}, \ldots, x_{n_k}, \ldots$, whose limit we denote by $s$; hence, $a \leqslant s \leqslant b$ because always $a \leqslant x_n \leqslant b$.

From the continuity of $f(x)$ at the point $s$, we deduce that $\lim_{k \to \infty} f(x_{n_k}) = f(s)$; thus the sequence $(f(x_{n_k}))_k$ is convergent, hence bounded. But this is impossible because, always, $n_k < |f(x_{n_k})|$.

Letting $U$ be the least upper bound of the range of values of $f$, we must show the existence of $x'$ in $[a, b]$ for which $f(x') = U$.

By definition, for every integer $n > 0$ there exists some number $s_n$ in $[a, b]$ such that $U - 1/n < f(s_n)$. Since the sequence $(s_n)$ is bounded (because its terms are contained in $[a, b]$), by the proposition on page 47 there exists a convergent subsequence $(s_{n_k})_k$, whose limit we denote by $x'$. Clearly, $x'$ is in $[a, b]$ and, from the comment on page 87, it follows that $f(x') = \lim_{k \to \infty} f(s_{n_k}) = U$.

The hypothesis that $f$ is continuous on the *closed* interval $[a, b]$ is essential. In fact, if it were the case of an interval which is not closed, the statement would be false in general, as we shall see in the following example.

The function $f(x) = 1/x$ is defined and continuous in the *open* interval $(0, 1)$, but it is not defined at the point 0. The range of values of this function is not bounded above and, thus, it does not have a least upper bound.

Similarly, the function $f$, which associates with every number $x$ in the open interval $(0, 1)$ the number $f(x) = x$, has a bounded range of values equal to $(0, 1)$; however, no number $x$ in the open interval $(0, 1)$ exists such that $f(x) = 0$ or $f(x) = 1$.

We now return to the question of continuity of the inverse function of a continuous function.

Let $y = f(x)$ be a *continuous* and strictly increasing function on the interval $[a, b]$; let $f(a) = \alpha$, $f(b) = \beta$, thus $[\alpha, \beta]$ is the range of values of $f$, as it follows from the intermediate value property of continuous functions.

Let $x = g(y)$ be the inverse function of $y = f(x)$; it has domain of definition equal to $[\alpha, \beta]$ (see page 67).

PROPOSITION. *With this hypothesis, g is also a continuous and strictly increasing function.*

To prove the continuity of $g$ at $y_0$, we must be careful to take into account that $y_0$ may be equal to $\alpha$ or $\beta$, but all cases may be treated together.

Let $y_0$ be an arbitrary point, $\alpha \leqslant y_0 \leqslant \beta$, and $x_0 = g(y_0)$.

Given any natural integer $L$, we consider the set of real numbers which are common to the intervals $[x_0 - 1/(L + 1), x_0 + 1/(L + 1)]$ and $[a, b]$; it is an interval, which we denote by $[a_1, b_1]$. Let $\alpha_1 = f(a_1)$, $\beta_1 = g(b_1)$; hence, by the intermediate value property, the continuous function $f$ transforms $[a_1, b_1]$ onto an interval $[\alpha_1, \beta_1]$ to which belongs $y_0$.

Taking a sufficiently large natural number $M$, every real number $y$ common to the intervals $[\alpha, \beta]$ and $(y_0 - 1/M, y_0 + 1/M)$ belongs to the interval $[\alpha_1, \beta_1]$; hence the inverse function $g$ transforms these numbers $y$ into numbers of $[a_1, b_1]$; that is, if $|y - y_0| < 1/M$ and $\alpha \leqslant y \leqslant \beta$, then

$$|g(y) - x_0| \leqslant \frac{1}{L + 1} < \frac{1}{L}.$$

This proves the continuity of the inverse function of $f$ on the interval $[\alpha, \beta]$.

As an easy exercise, state and prove a corresponding result when $f$ is defined, for example, on a half-line $[a, +\infty)$.

We now give more examples of continuous functions.

In Chapter 3, while defining the operation $\alpha^{1/q}$, when $\alpha > 0$ is a real number and $q > 0$ is an integer, we stated that a justification for this definition could be found using properties related to continuous functions.

Indeed, as we know, the function $f(x) = x^q$ is a continuous strictly increasing function, defined on the half-line $[0, \infty)$; by the intermediate value property, the range of values of $f$ is again $[0, \infty)$. Its inverse function $g$ is therefore defined on $[0, \infty)$, strictly increasing and continuous. For every real number $\alpha > 0$, the value $g(\alpha) = \beta$ is exactly that unique real number such that $f(\beta) = \beta^q = \alpha$, that is, $\beta = \alpha^{1/q}$.

The restriction of the function $y = \sin x$ to the interval $[-\pi/2, +\pi/2]$ is a continuous and strictly increasing function with range of values $[-1, +1]$. Its inverse function is denoted by $x = \arcsin y$, has domain of definition $[-1, +1]$, range of values $[-\pi/2, +\pi/2]$, and it is also continuous and strictly increasing.

Using also the notion of function of function, we obtain many more examples of continuous functions, such as the following ones.

$$y = \sqrt{x^2 - 3}, \text{ continuous for } x^2 \geqslant 3$$
$$y = \sqrt{1 + x} - \sqrt{1 - x}, \text{ continuous for } -1 \leqslant x \leqslant +1$$
$$y = \text{Arc} \sin (x^3 - 5), \text{ continuous for } -1 \leqslant x^3 - 5 \leqslant +1.$$

## Exercises

1. For each of the functions in Exercises 1 and 3 on pp. 70 and 71, find the points where the function is not continuous.

2. Let $f$ be the function defined as follows: $f(x) = 1/q$ when $x = p/q$, rational number in its irreducible representation; $f(x) = 0$, when $x$ is not rational.

Show that $f(x)$ is continuous at every point $x$ which is irrational, and discontinuous at every point $x$ which is rational.

3. Let $f$ be the function defined as follows:

If $x$ is rational, $0 \leqslant x \leqslant 1$, then $f(x) = x$;
If $x$ is irrational, $0 \leqslant x \leqslant 1$, then $f(x) = 1 - x$.

Prove that $f$ assumes every value between 0, 1 once and only once; however, $f$ is discontinuous at every point $x$, $0 \leqslant x \leqslant 1$, except for $x_0 = 1/2$.

4. Show that the function $f$ defined as

$$f(x) = \sin \frac{1}{x}, \text{ when } x \neq 0$$
$$f(x) = 0, \text{ when } x = 0,$$

is continuous at every point, except $x = 0$. There is no limit of $f$ when $x$ tends to 0. Every interval $(-1/N, 1/N)$ contains infinitely many real numbers $x$ such that $f(x) = 1$ (least upper bound of $f$) as well as infinitely many real numbers $x'$ such that $f(x') = -1$ (greatest lower bound of $f$). Thus, there exist sequences of real numbers $(x_n)$, $(x'_n)$, such that $\lim x_n = \lim x'_n = 0$ and $\lim f(x_n) = 1$, $\lim f(x'_n) = -1$.

5. If $f$, $g$ are continuous functions on the real line, prove that the functions $x \rightarrow \max \{f(x), g(x)\}$ and $x \rightarrow \min \{f(x), g(x)\}$ are also continuous functions on the real line.

6. Prove that if $f$ is a real-valued continuous function defined on the set of real numbers and has the property that $f(x_1 + x_2) = f(x_1) + f(x_2)$ for any real numbers $x_1$, $x_2$, then there exists a real number $a$ such that $f(x) = ax$ for every real number $x$.

# 9

# Uniform Continuity

In this chapter we shall consider the notion of uniform continuity, which often presents some difficulty.

An understanding of the notions of the two previous chapters is essential to proceed with this one.

Certain properties of sets of real numbers, referring to "compactness," are intimately connected with the uniform continuity. Logically, they should be studied at the end of Chapter 4, even before the concepts of limits and continuity. Nevertheless, since their first application appears here, we have postponed their presentation until now, rather than give the impression that they are artificially included. Moreover, it is convenient to stress that, historically, the notion of compactness sprung partly from a detailed analysis of the uniform continuity.

Thus, this chapter is divided into three parts: (1) some properties of sets of real numbers, the HEINE-BOREL theorem and the notion of compactness; (2) uniform continuity; (3) an application of uniform continuity.

## HEINE-BOREL Theorem and Compactness

We begin with the notion of COVERING of an interval.

Our presentation will not be a general one since, at every step, we wish to keep close contact with our intuition.

Let $[a, b]$ be a given *closed* interval. If for every real number $x$ of this interval we associate the *open* interval $(x - 1/N, x + 1/N)$, where $N$ is a given natural number, then it is clear that taking the union of the intervals $(x - 1/N, x + 1/N)$ corresponding to all the points $x$ of $[a, b]$ we obtain a set which "covers" the interval $[a, b]$; that means that every point of [a, b] is in some of the considered intervals (usually in more than one). Clearly, each $x \in [a, b]$ is in the interval $(x - 1/N, x + 1/N)$.

What we have just done is absolutely trivial, but will serve to explain the notion of an open covering of a closed interval.

Let [a, b] be a closed interval, and consider a family $C$ of open intervals whose union covers (that is, contains) the closed interval [a, b]; in other words, every real number $x \in [a, b]$ is in some of the intervals of the collection $C$. Then, we say that the collection $C$ of open intervals is an *open covering* of [a, b] (or simply a covering of [a, b]).

We notice that a covering may be formed by an infinite number of intervals, as in the first example, where the covering had as many open intervals as there were points in [a, b].*

Now we give another example.

Let [a, b] be the interval [0, 3] and to every rational number $r$ in [a, b] we associate the open interval $(r - 1/2, r + 1/2)$. This infinite collection of open intervals constitutes a covering of [0, 3]; in fact, if $x$ is rational, for example $x = r$, then it belongs to $(r - 1/2, r + 1/2)$; if, however, $x$ is irrational, there exists surely a rational number $r_0$ approximating $x$ by less than 1/2, so $x$ is in $(r_0 - 1/2, r_0 + 1/2)$.

It happens that in this covering of [0, 3] there are still many more intervals than we need to cover [0, 3], and every point of [0, 3] belongs to an infinite number of intervals of the type $(r - 1/2, r + 1/2)$. We are thus led to investigate whether, by omitting intervals of this collection, we still have a covering of [0, 3].

Of course, this is the case in the above example. We need only consider the intervals

$$\left(\frac{1}{3} - \frac{1}{2}, \frac{1}{3} + \frac{1}{2}\right), \quad \left(1 - \frac{1}{2}, 1 + \frac{1}{2}\right), \quad \left(\frac{5}{3} - \frac{1}{2}, \frac{5}{3} + \frac{1}{2}\right),$$

$$\left(\frac{5}{2} - \frac{1}{2}, \frac{5}{2} + \frac{1}{2}\right), \quad \left(3 - \frac{1}{2}, 3 + \frac{1}{2}\right).$$

Clearly, there are infinitely many other possible choices of coverings extracted from the given infinite covering.

An important fact, which we stress, was the possibility of choosing, in this example, a *finite number* of open intervals making a covering of [0, 3]. This was intuitive because [0, 3] is an interval of finite length and the given covering was formed by intervals of constant length 1.

---

* Thus, in the sense explained in Appendix B, the collection of open sets constituting the covering does not need to be countable, since the set of all numbers $x$, such that $a \leq x \leq b$, is infinite, uncountable.

Therefore, in investigating whether there exists a finite "subcovering" of a given covering, no doubt arises in the cases where all the intervals of the given covering have a constant length or, at least, a length larger than some fixed strictly positive number.

However, we may imagine a covering of $[a, b]$ formed by an infinite number of intervals, some of them as short in length as we like. In this case, our argument does not work, and we need more powerful means to decide the question. We shall use essentially the BOLZANO-WEIERSTRASS theorem and method of proof to answer this problem.

THEOREM (HEINE-BOREL). *Let $[a, b]$ be a closed interval, and let $C$ be a collection of open intervals constituting an open covering of $[a, b]$. Then it is possible to select a finite number of intervals in the collection $C$, let us say $I_1, I_2, \ldots, I_m$, such that these intervals form still a covering of $[a, b]$.*

*Proof.* If the theorem is not true, there exists some covering $C$ of $[a, b]$ by *open* intervals, in such a way that no selection of a finite number of these intervals will cover $[a, b]$. We now proceed as in the proof of the Bolzano-Weierstrass theorem.

Let $c_1$ be the middle point of $[a, b]$, and consider the intervals $[a, c_1]$, $[c_1, b]$. Since $[a, c_1]$ and $[c_1, b]$ are both contained in the interval $[a, b]$, the given collection $C$ of intervals is again a covering of $[a, c_1]$ as well as of $[c_1, b]$. We claim (1) either it is not possible to select a finite number of the given intervals so as to obtain a finite covering of $[a, c_1]$; or (2) it is not possible to select a finite number of the given intervals so as to obtain a finite covering of $[c_1, b]$.

Otherwise, there exist intervals $I_1, \ldots, I_{m_1}$ among the given ones, whose union covers $[a, c_1]$, and also, there exist intervals $I_{m_1+1}, \ldots, I_m$, among the given ones, whose union covers $[c_1, b]$. As $[a, b]$ is the union of $[a, c_1]$ and $[c_1, b]$, then all the intervals $I_1, \ldots, I_{m_1}, I_{m_1+1}, \ldots, I_m$ will constitute a covering of $[a, b]$, which is actually a finite covering. Recalling our assumption that no such finite covering exists, we have arrived at a contradiction. Thus, our claim has been verified.

Let us give new names to the intervals $[a, c_1]$, $[c_1, b]$. We shall call $[a_1, b_1]$ *the leftmost* of these two intervals with the property that no finite covering of $[a_1, b_1]$ may be selected from the given collection $C$ of intervals.

We are now in the same situation with respect to $[a_1, b_1]$ as we were previously with $[a, b]$, and we know also that $a \leqslant a_1 < b_1 \leqslant b$.

Repeating the same argument, starting from $[a_1, b_1]$, and dividing it by its middle point $c_2$, we conclude that there exists one of the half-intervals $[a_1, c_2]$ or $[c_2, b_1]$ with the property that no finite covering of it extracted from $C$ may be chosen. Again, we call $[a_2, b_2]$ the leftmost of the above two intervals having this property and, by construction, we have $a \leqslant a_1 \leqslant a_2 < b_2 \leqslant b_1 \leqslant b$.

This process may be repeated indefinitely, and we obtain a sequence of closed intervals $[a, b]$, $[a_1, b_1]$, $[a_2, b_2]$, ..., $[a_n, b_n]$, ..., each such interval having length equal to one half of the length of the preceding one.

The bounded monotone increasing sequence $a \leqslant a_1 \leqslant a_2 \leqslant \ldots \leqslant a_n \leqslant \ldots$ has a limit $x_0$; this is equal to the limit $x_0'$ of the bounded monotone decreasing sequence $b \geqslant b_1 \geqslant b_2 \geqslant \ldots \geqslant b_n \geqslant \ldots$ because $a_n \leqslant x_0 \leqslant x_0' \leqslant b_n$, for every index $n$ and $|x_0' - x_0| \leqslant |b_n - a_n| = |b - a|/2^n$ for every index $n$. Thus, the only possibility is that $|x_0' - x_0| = 0$, that is, $x_0 = x_0'$.

Since $x_0$ is in $[a, b]$ and $\mathcal{C}$ is a covering of $[a, b]$ by open intervals, there exists some of these intervals, for instance, $I = (\alpha, \beta)$, which contains $x_0$. Let $\epsilon$ be the smallest of the numbers $x_0 - \alpha$, $\beta - x_0$, so $\epsilon > 0$. Since $\lim\limits_{n \to \infty} a_n = \lim\limits_{n \to \infty} b_n = x_0$, given $\epsilon > 0$, there exists an integer $n_1$ such that if $m \geqslant n_1$ then $|a_n - x_0| < \epsilon$, and also an integer $n_1'$ such that if $m \geqslant n_1'$ then $|b_n - x_0| < \epsilon$. Taking $m \geqslant n_1$ and $m \geqslant n_1'$, we have both inequalities $|a_n - x_0| < \epsilon$, $|b_n - x_0| < \epsilon$. This means that the interval $[a_n, b_n]$ is contained in $I = (\alpha, \beta)$. But this is a contradiction, for here is one of the intervals $[a_n, b_n]$, obtained in our recursive process, which has been selected so as not to be covered by a finite number of the given intervals, and nevertheless it appears as covered already by the one interval $I_s$.

This contradiction shows that the theorem is true.

This theorem of Heine and Borel does not appear as an isolated result. On the contrary, it is one of the most fundamental properties of the real number system. Actually, a whole theory may be developed based on this theorem, establishing several other equivalent formulations as well as their corollaries.

Historically, the proof of this theorem and its immediate consequences have been, together with Cauchy's general convergence theorem, some of the crucial steps in opening the road for the modern analysis.

Nowadays, the study of the notions of limit, continuity, and uniform continuity is made in quite an abstract frame, as a part of the general set topology. The purpose is to treat several instances in only one development: for example, continuity properties of real valued functions of $n$ real variables, vector valued functions of $n$ real or complex variables (the values being $m$-dimensional vectors with real or complex components) and, more generally, functions on METRIC SPACES, which are sets endowed with a "distance" generalizing the usual distance in the Euclidean three-dimensional space.

This brief digression suggests how small the field is that we have been examining in this book. However, we emphasize that the basic ideas dealt with here are some of the most useful and precious ones in mathematics. When they are repeated in their most varied form, and are generalized or adapted to different situations, they are as fundamental as a master beam in an entire building.

Now we return to the notion of compactness.

A set $S$ of real numbers is said to be COMPACT when, given any covering of $S$ by a collection $\mathcal{C}$ of open intervals, it is possible to select a finite number of these intervals which still cover $S$.

Thus, the Heine-Borel theorem may be also formulated as follows.

*Every closed interval $[a, b]$ is a compact set in the real number system.*

However, there are compact sets which are not closed intervals. For example, any set composed of only a finite number of points is compact.

The following are the main properties of compact sets in the real line.

(1) *A subset $S$ of the real line is compact if and only if, from any given sequence $(a_n)$ of numbers of $S$, it is possible to extract a convergent subsequence $(a_{n_k})_k$ whose limit is in $S$.*

Comparing this statement with the proposition on page 47, we see that a bounded set $S$ will be compact, provided it has the following property: *the limit of any convergent sequence of elements of $S$ belongs to $S$.*

Any set $S$ of real numbers with this property is called a CLOSED SET. Clearly, every closed interval is a closed set.

This helps to motivate the next proposition.

(2) *A set of real numbers is compact if and only if it is bounded and closed.*

In particular, an interval I is compact if and only if it is a closed interval.

These results are not used in this book and their proofs are proposed as exercises. We point out that several propositions concerning closed intervals have been generalized for abstract spaces, using compact sets instead of closed intervals. An example is the generalized Heine-Borel theorem.

In this connection, consult the bibliography at the end of this volume.

## Uniform Continuity

Let $f$ be a function defined and continuous on a set $S$ of real numbers.

The continuity of $f$ at the point $x_0$ of $S$ means, by definition, that given any natural number $N$, as large as we like, there exists a natural number $M$, such that if $x$ is in $S$ and $|x - x_0| < 1/M$ then $|f(x) - f(x_0)| < 1/N$.

We notice that, given the number $N$, the number $M$ is determined by $N$; in other words, $M$ depends on $N$.

Now, if $x_1$ is another point of $S$, then $f$ is also continuous at the point $x_1$ by hypothesis. So, given any natural number $N$, there exists some natural number $M$ associated to $N$ as it is prescribed in the definition of continuity at the point $x_1$. In general, if we give a number $N$, the continuity at the point $x_0$ determines a certain $M_0$, and the continuity at the point $x_1$ deter-

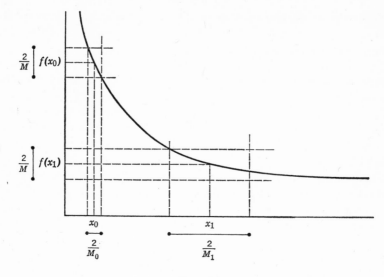

Figure 11

mines a certain $M_1$. There is no reason why the numbers $M_0$, $M_1$, thus determined, be equal. Therefore, for the given integer $N$, the associated integer $M$ depends also on the point on which we consider the continuity. Summarizing, $M$ depends (1) on the given integer $N$, and (2) on the point $x$ on which $f'$ is continuous. This may be seen in Figure 11.

We may express this dependency, denoting by $M_x(N)$ the integer associated to the given integer $N$, at the point $x$ of $S$. For example, $M_2(35) = 12$ means that for the given function $f$, continuous at the point $x = 2$, and for the given integer $N = 35$, we have: $|x - 2| < 1/12$ implies $|f(x) - f(2)| < 1/35$.

We now discuss the manner in which the integer $M_x(N)$ depends on the point $x$ of $S$.

Consider a *fixed* $N$. For every point $x$ where $f$ is continuous, we may determine a natural number $M = M_x(N)$ which depends on $x$ (and, of course, on $N$). Consider the collection of numbers $1/M_x(N)$ thus obtained, when $x$ varies in the set $S$ on which $f$ is continuous. This is a collection of numbers that are *strictly* positive. Two cases may arise: (1) the greatest lower bound of these numbers is 0, or (2) the greatest lower bound of these numbers is strictly larger than 0.

In the first case, there are numbers $1/M_x$ as close to 0 as we like. In the second case, there exists a number, namely the greatest lower bound $\delta = \inf \{1/M_x\}$, with the property $0 < \delta \leqslant 1/M_x$ for every point $x \in S$.

Note that if $x$ is any number in $S$ such that $|x - x_0| < \delta$ then also $|x - x_0| < 1/M_{x_0}$ (whatever be the point $x_0$ in $S$); thus, by the continuity of $f$ in $x_0$, we conclude that $|f(x) - f(x_0)| < 1/N$.

Therefore, what we have just done amounts simply to determining a sufficiently narrow vertical strip, over the interval $(x_0 - \delta, x_0 + \delta)$, with the property that the graph of the function $f$ in this strip is inside the rectangle limited by the horizontal strip determined by the interval $(f(x_0) - 1/N, f(x_0) + 1/N)$. The most important feature was that this number $\delta$ may serve as well for any other point $x_1, x_2, \ldots$ where the function $f$ is continuous.

Thus, in the second case, given an horizontal strip of breadth $2/N$, around any value of the function $f$, it is possible to find a vertical strip of breadth $2\delta$, such that the values of $f$ at point $x'$, $x''$ in the vertical strip will be inside the horizontal strip. In other words, if $|x' - x''| < 2\delta$ then $|f(x') - f(x'')| < 2/N$. This number $\delta$ depends only on $N$, since the same number $\delta$ is good for any point $x$ in the domain of definition of $f(x)$.

Clearly, the above statement is equivalent to the following one: in the second case, given any natural number $N$, there exists a strictly positive real number $\delta$ (which depends on $N$), such that if $|x' - x''| < \delta$, with $x'$ and $x''$ in $S$, then $|f(x') - f(x'')| < 1/N$. We have merely changed notation: our new $\delta$ replaces the previous $2\delta$, and the new $N$ replaces the old $N/2$.

We have, therefore, justified the following definition.

*The function $f$ is* UNIFORMLY CONTINUOUS *on the set $S$ when, given any natural number $N$, there exists a strictly positive real number $\delta$ (which depends on $N$), such that if $x'$, $x''$ are in $S$ and $|x' - x''| < \delta$ then $|f(x') - f(x'')| < 1/N$.*

Now we comment on this definition.

First, we may replace the real number $\delta$ by a number of the form $1/M$ by taking a sufficiently large integer $M$, so that $1/M < \delta$. From now on, we shall pass over this type of trivial consideration, since we already have noticed how irrelevant it is to choose a number of the form $\delta$ or $1/M$; similarly, we shall skip the consideration of strict or nonstrict inequalities in the definitions of neighborhoods and limits, as this also is secondary.

Another more important observation is that the notion of uniform continuity is, in one respect, essentially distinct from the notion of continuity. We have defined the continuity of a function at any point of its domain of definition. Thus, the notion of continuity is of LOCAL character, referring to the behavior of the function in the neighborhood of a given point. Even when we have introduced the concept of a continuous function on a set, all we have done has been to consider the continuity of the function at every point of the set, without establishing any *comparison* between the continuity at different points.

On the contrary, with the notion of uniform continuity on a set $S$, we actually compare the continuity of $f$ at the different points of the set. Therefore, the notion of uniform continuity is not of local nature but, instead, of GLOBAL character. It is also clear that if a function $f$ is uniformly continuous on a set $S$, it is also uniformly continuous on every part of $S$.

Finally, to motivate the notion of uniform continuity we have assumed that the function $f$ was *continuous* at every point of the set $S$. However, in the actual definition of uniform continuity, we do not make this assumption. It is very easy to prove that if a function (not assumed continuous) is uniformly continuous on the set $S$, it is continuous on every point of $S$. This proof is suggested as an exercise.

Next, we shall give some examples of functions that are uniformly continuous and of others that are not.

EXAMPLE 1. Let $f(x) = a$ be a constant function. Then, $f$ is uniformly continuous on the whole real line.

EXAMPLE 2. Let $f(x) = x$. Then $f$ is uniformly continuous on the whole real line. We must verify that, given any integer $N > 0$, there exists an integer $M > 0$ such that if $|x' - x''| < 1/M$ then $|f(x') - f(x'')| < 1/N$. This is clear, since $f(x') = x'$, $f(x'') = x''$, and we only need to take $M = N$.

EXAMPLE 3. The function $f(x) = x^q$ (where $q$ is a given integer, $q > 0$) is uniformly continuous on every interval $I$ (open, or closed, but necessarily bounded). Let $I = [a, b]$ and consider any natural number $N$; if $M > 0$ is any integer and $|x' - x''| < 2/M$ then

$$
\begin{aligned}
|x'^q - x''^q| &= |x' - x''| \cdot |x'^{q-1} + x'^{q-2} \cdot x'' + \ldots + x' \cdot x''^{q-2} + x''^{q-1}| \\
&< (1/M)(|x'|^{q-1} + |x'|^{q-2} \cdot |x''| + \ldots + |x'| \cdot |x''|^{q-2} + |x''|^{q-1}) \\
&< (1/M)q \cdot k^{q-1}
\end{aligned}
$$

where $k = \max\{|a|, |b|\}$ (see the computation on page 74). Therefore, if we choose $M$ so large that $M > Nqk^{q-1}$, it follows from $x'$, $x''$ in $[a, b]$, $|x' - x''| < 1/M$ that $|x'^q - x''^q| < 1/N$.

Note that if we had chosen, instead of an interval (which is necessarily bounded), the whole line, then the function $f(x) = x^q$ (with $q > 1$) would not be uniformly continuous. This may be deduced from the above discussion, since we have seen that the value of $M$, associated to $N$, has to be larger than some expression involving $k$, which in turn becomes larger and larger as we consider bigger intervals $[a, b]$. Therefore, no finite value of $M$ (associated to a given $N$) can be found which would serve for the whole line.

The reason for this behavior is easy to understand: the farther from 0, the faster the function $f(x) = x^q$ grows in absolute value.

This example shows clearly that the notion of uniform continuity refers essentially to some set (contained in the domain of definition of the function). A given function may well be uniformly continuous on an interval without being uniformly continuous on a larger one.

The following proposition is similar to one already established for limits and continuous functions; we shall omit its proof.

PROPOSITION. *Let $f$, $g$ be functions uniformly continuous on a set $S$. Then, $f + g$, $f - g$, and $f \cdot g$ are also uniformly continuous on the set $S$.*

With the same hypothesis, we cannot conclude, however, that $f/g$ is uniformly continuous on $S$. We know that it is not even true that $f/g$ is continuous on all the points of $S$, since we can only insure the continuity whenever $g(x_0) \neq 0$. With regard to the uniform continuity, we may assert that $f/g$ *is uniformly continuous on every interval $I$, contained in the set $S$, for which $g(x) \neq 0$, including the end points of $I$.* Proof of this follows easily from the theorem below and the result of page 87.

Also we want to show how to construct a function which is continuous on an interval without being uniformly continuous there. It is essential that this interval cannot be a *closed* interval.

The function $f(x) = 1/x$ is continuous on the *open* interval $(0, 1)$ since, as we know, the only point of discontinuity lies at $x = 0$, where the denominator vanishes. However, this function $f(x) = 1/x$ is not uniformly continuous on $(0, 1)$. Intuitively we may expect this behavior, because $f$ grows more and more rapidly as $x$ approaches 0. In a more precise way, given a natural number, for example $N = 1$, we want to show that, for any arbitrary integer $M$, it is possible to find points $x'$, $x''$ (sufficiently close to 0) in the interval $(0, 1)$ in such a way that $|x' - x''| < 1/M$, but $|f(x') - f(x'')| = |1/x' - 1/x''| \geqslant 1 = 1/N$. Therefore, no number $M$ will serve for the condition in the definition of uniform continuity. The choice of $x'$ and $x''$ is quite simple; we take $x' = 1/2M$, $x'' = 1/M$, then $|x' - x''| = 1/2M < 1/M$; however $|1/x' - 1/x''| = 2M - M = M \geqslant 1 = 1/N$.

We can easily explain why this situation appears: 0 is a point of discontinuity of the function $f(x) = 1/x$ and $\lim_{x \to 0+} 1/x = +\infty$. If, however, $f$ would still be continuous at the end points of the interval $(a, b)$, then $f$ would be continuous in the closed interval $[a, b]$, and this situation would not take place. That is stated in the following fundamental theorem.

THEOREM. *Every function f, defined and continuous on a closed interval* $[a, b]$, *is uniformly continuous on* $[a, b]$.

To prove the theorem we must show that, given any natural number $N$, there exists a natural number $M$ (depending only on $N$) such that if $x'$, $x''$ are in $[a, b]$ and $|x' - x''| < 1/M$ then $|f(x') - f(x'')| < 1/N$.

Let us use the hypothesis that the function $f$ is continuous on every point $x$ in $[a, b]$. This means that, given any natural number $N$, associated with $2N$ and every point $x$ in $[a, b]$, we can find an integer $L(x)$ (which depends on $N$ and $x$) such that if $s$ is in $[a, b]$ and $|s - x| < 1/L(x)$ then $|f(s) - f(x)| < 1/2N$.

In this way, we may associate to every point $x$ in $[a, b]$ an open interval containing $x$, namely $(x - 1/2L(x), x + 1/2L(x))$, and the collection of open intervals thus obtained is an open covering of the interval $[a, b]$.

We are therefore in a situation where we may apply the Heine-Borel theorem. It asserts the existence of a finite number of such intervals whose union still covers $[a, b]$. Let us call these intervals

$$I_1 = (x_1 - 1/2L_1, x_1 + 1/2L_1), \ldots, I_m = (x_m - 1/2L_m, x_m + 1/2L_m),$$

where for simplicity we have also written $L_1 = L(x_1), \ldots, L_m = L(x_m)$.

Now we choose an integer $M$ so large that $M > 2L_1, \ldots, M > 2L_m$, hence $1/M < 1/2L_1, \ldots, 1/M < 1/2L_m$.

Let $x'$, $x''$ be any two points of $[a, b]$ such that $|x' - x''| < 1/M$. Since the intervals $I_1, \ldots, I_m$ constitute a covering of $[a, b]$, $x'$ is in some of these intervals (for example, $x' \in I_1$), hence $|x' - x_1| < 1/2L_1 < 1/L_1$. Moreover,

$$|x_1 - x''| = |(x_1 - x') + (x' - x'')| \leqslant |x_1 - x'| + |x' - x''|$$
$$< 1/2L_1 + 1/M < 1/L_1.$$

Therefore, by the choice of $L_1$, we deduce that

$$|f(x_1) - f(x')| < 1/2N, \quad |f(x_1) - f(x'')| < 1/2N$$

and, combining these inequalities, we have

$$|f(x') - f(x'')| = |(f(x') - f(x_1)) + (f(x_1) - f(x''))|$$
$$\leq |f(x') - f(x_1)| + |f(x_1) - f(x'')| < \frac{1}{2N} + \frac{1}{2N} = \frac{1}{N}$$

Since $M$ was independent of the point $x$ in $[a, b]$, it follows that $f$ is uniformly continuous on $[a, b]$.

Now we apply this theorem.

Let $f$ be a given function, and $S$ a set contained in the domain of definition of $f$. When $x$ varies in the set $S$, the corresponding values of the function constitute a set of numbers, which we denote by $f(S)$.

Our purpose is to define the OSCILLATION of $f$ on the set $S$. If $f(S)$ is not bounded above or below, we say that $f$ has *infinite oscillation* on the set $S$.

If, however, $f(S)$ is a bounded set of real numbers then, as we know, there exists the least upper bound $\mu$ and the greatest lower bound $\lambda$ of this set $f(S)$; clearly $\lambda \leqslant \mu$. *The difference $\mu - \lambda$ is called the oscillation of f on the set S.* We denote it by $\Omega$, and we have $\Omega \geqslant 0$; clearly, $\Omega = 0$ if and only if $f$ is constant on the set $S$.

To indicate that the oscillation depends on the set $S$ as well as on the function $f$, we may use the more complete notation $\Omega_f(S)$.

We may now prove the following result, which tells us, intuitively, that the graph of any uniformly continuous function on a bounded set cannot increase and decrease infinitely often unless the oscillation decreases to zero.

PROPOSITION. *Let f be a function, uniformly continuous on the bounded set S. For every natural number N, it is possible to divide the set S into a finite number of parts, $S_1$, $S_2$, . . ., $S_n$, in such a way that, in each of these parts, the oscillation of f is, at most, $1/N$.*

By hypothesis, given the integer $N > 0$, there exists a natural number $M$, such that if $x'$, $x'$ are in $S$ and $|x' - x''| < 1/M$ then $|f(x') - f(x'')| < 1/N$.

Since $S$ is bounded, it is contained in some closed intervals $[a, b]$. Consider the following points in the interval $[a, b]$:

$$x_1 = a + \frac{1}{M + 1}, \quad x_2 = x_1 + \frac{1}{M + 1}, \quad x_3 = x_2 + \frac{1}{M + 1},$$

and so on; by the Archimedean property of the real line, there exists some index $n$ such that $x_{n-1} < b \leqslant x_n$. Let $S_1$ be the set of points of $S$ common to $[a, x_1]$ and, similarly, let $S_i$ be the set of points of $S$ common to $[x_{i-1}, x_i]$, for every index $i = 1, \ldots, n - 1$.

In each of the sets $S_1$, $S_2$, . . ., $S_n$ the oscillation of $f$ is, at most, equal to $1/N$ because if $x'$, $x''$ are points in the same of the above sets, then $|x' - x''| \leqslant 1/(M + 1) < 1/M$ and, therefore, $|f(x') - f(x'')| < 1/N$.

We emphasize that if the set $S$ is not bounded, the above proposition would not be true. For example, the function $f(x) = x$ is uniformly continuous on the whole real line, which cannot be divided into a finite number of parts, on each of which $f$ has oscillation, at most, 1.

To avoid any misinterpretation, we must make it clear that the possibility is not excluded that the graph of a uniformly continuous function $f$ on a bounded set $S$ oscillates infinitely often, in the sense that the function increases and decreases infinitely many times; by the theorem, it must be true that, considering smaller and smaller parts $S'$ of $S$, the oscillation $\Omega_{S'}(f)$ will ultimately become less than any given quantity.

For example, let $f(x) = x.\sin 1/x$, defined for $x$ in the closed interval $[-1, 1]$. This function is continuous at every point of $[-1, 1]$, even at the

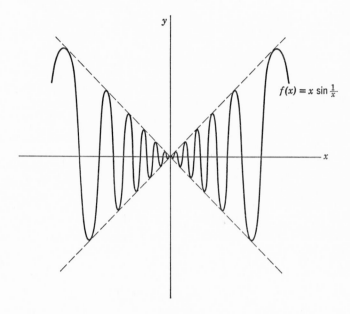

$$f(x) = x \sin \tfrac{1}{x}$$

Figure 12

point $x = 0$, as may be easily verified; therefore, it is uniformly continuous; thus, we may apply the above proposition and conclude that, given any integer $N > 0$, it is possible to find a subdivision of $[-1, 1]$ into intervals, on each of which $f$ has oscillation, at most, $1/N$. This subdivision is given by considering all the intervals of type $[m/N, (m+1)/N]$ where $m = -N, -N+1, \ldots, 0, 1, \ldots, N-1$.

However, a glance at the graph of $f$ (Figure 12) shows that in any interval $(-1/M, 1/M)$ around 0 the function increases and decreases infinitely often; but, each time, the "peaks" of its graph become smaller and smaller.

On page 87, we stated a condition for the continuity of a function $f$ in terms of sequences; roughly speaking, the function $f$ is continuous exactly when it transforms convergent sequences into convergent sequences.

Now we present a similar result for uniformly continuous functions.

PROPOSITION. *If a function $f$ is uniformly continuous on the set $S$, if $(x_n)$ is any Cauchy sequence of elements in $S$, then $(f(x_n))$ is also a Cauchy sequence. Conversely, if a function $f$, defined on a* BOUNDED *set $S$ transforms Cauchy sequences of elements of $S$ into Cauchy sequences, then $f$ is uniformly continuous on $S$.*

Let $f$ be uniformly continuous on the set $S$, and let $(x_n)$ be a Cauchy sequence of elements in $S$. Given the natural number $N$, there exists an integer $M > 0$ such that if $x'$, $x'' \in S$ and $|x' - x''| < 1/M$ then $|f(x') - f(x'')| < 1/N$. But, associated with the integer $M > 0$, there exists an index $n_0$ such that if $m, n \geqslant n_0$ then $|x_m - x_n| < 1/M$; therefore, $|f(x_n) - f(x_m)| < 1/N$, which shows that $(f(x_n))$ is a Cauchy sequence.

On the other hand, assume that the function $f$ is not uniformly continuous on the bounded set $S$. The negation of uniform continuity may be thus expressed: there exists a natural number $N$ such that for every integer $n > 0$ there exist points $x'_n, x''_n$ in $S$ such that $|x'_n - x''_n| < 1/n$, however $|f(x'_n) - f(x''_n)| > 1/N$.

Since $S$ is bounded, it is possible to extract a convergent subsequence of $(x'_n)$, namely $(x'_{n_k})_k$; it is not implied, however, that the limit $x_0$ of $(x'_{n_k})_k$ belongs to $S$; at any rate, $(x'_{n_k})_k$ is a Cauchy sequence. In the same way, there exists a Cauchy sequence $(x''_{n_k})_k$, having the same limit $x_0$, as it follows from the inequality

$$|x''_{n_k} - x_0| = |(x''_{n_k} - x'_{n_k}) + (x'_{n_k} - x_0)| \leq |x''_{n_k} - x'_{n_k}| + |x'_{n_k} - x_0|$$

since both

$$|x''_{n_k} - x'_{n_k}|, \quad |x'_{n_k} - x_0|$$

may be made arbitrarily small.

Therefore, the sequence $(x_k)$, where

$$x_1 = x'_{n_1}, x_2 = x''_{n_1}, \ldots, x_{2k-1} = x'_{n_k}, x_{2k} = x''_{n_k}, \ldots,$$

obtained by mixing together the two convergent subsequences $(x'_{n_k})_k$, $(x''_{n_k})_k$, is again a Cauchy sequence, as may be easily verified.

By hypothesis, we deduce that $(f(x_k))$ is also a Cauchy sequence; thus, given the natural number $N$, there exists an index $k_0$ such that if $k, k' \geqslant k_0$ then $|f(x_k) - f(x_{k'})| < 1/N$. However, this is not the case, since for every index $k_0$ we have

$$|f(x_{2k_0-1}) - f(x_{2k_0})| = |f(x'_{n_{k_0}}) - f(x''_{n_{k_0}})| > \frac{1}{N},$$

This shows that $f$ must be uniformly continuous on the bounded set $S$.

*Note:* The second part of the proposition is not true if we drop the hypothesis that $S$ be a bounded set. From the previous computation (page 102), the function $f(x) = x^q$ ($q$ natural number, $q > 1$) is uniformly continuous on every closed interval; nevertheless, it is not uniformly continuous on the whole real line. But, since every Cauchy sequence is necessarily bounded, the function $f$ transforms Cauchy sequences into Cauchy sequences.

Now we give a useful theorem of extension of uniformly continuous functions. Its main value will be illustrated in the definition of the exponential functions.

Often, in trying to define a function on the real line (or some interval), we first define it on the integers and then on the rational numbers. If we are able to show that the function $f$ is uniformly continuous on the set of all rational numbers in an interval $I$, then our next theorem implies that there exists one unique function, defined also for the irrational numbers of the interval $I$, which coincides with $f$ on the rational numbers of $I$ and which is continuous on $I$; it will be even uniformly continuous on $I$. The main point here is that $f$ is uniformly continuous on the set of all rational numbers of $I$, and every irrational number is a limit of a Cauchy sequence of rational numbers; thus, the preceding proposition implies that $f$ transforms this Cauchy sequence into another one, whose limit will be the value of the new function at the irrational point.

More generally, we state the theorem.

THEOREM (PRINCIPLE OF EXTENSION OF UNIFORMLY CONTINUOUS FUNCTIONS). *Let $S$ be a set, and $S'$ a part of $S$ such that every point of $S$ is an accumulation point for the set $S'$. Let $f'$ be a function, uniformly continuous on the set $S'$. Then there exists one and only one continuous function $f$, defined on the set $S$, such that $f(x) = f'(x)$ for every $x$ in $S'$. Moreover, if $S$ is bounded, then $f$ is uniformly continuous on $S$.*

First, we notice that if there is, at all, a continuous function $f$ defined on the set $S$, with the property stated, then, for every element $x \in S$ and for every sequence $(x_n')$ of elements of $S'$ such that $\lim x_n' = x$ (which exist since $x$ is an accumulation point for $S'$), we must have $f(x) = \lim f(x_n') = \lim f'(x_n')$ (since $x_n'$ is in $S'$). Thus, $f(x)$ must be the unique limit of the convergent sequence $(f'(x_n'))$ and, consequently, only one continuous function $f$ may exist with the required property.

We have also learned how we should define the value of $f$ at every point $x \in S$. Precisely, if $x \in S$, it is an accumulation point for $S'$, hence there exists a sequence $(x_n')$ of elements of $S'$ such that $\lim x_n' = x$; therefore, $(x_n')$ is a Cauchy sequence. Since $f'$ is uniformly continuous on $S'$ then, by the previous proposition, $(f'(x_n'))$ is a Cauchy sequence. Hence, there exists a real number $y = \lim f'(x_n')$. We define $f(x) = y$.

Now, we must justify this definition by showing that if $(z_n')$ is another Cauchy sequence in $S'$ such that $\lim z_n' = x$, then $\lim f'(z_n') = \lim f'(x_n')$. This follows from the uniform continuity of $f'$ on $S'$. Given any natural number $N$, there exists an integer $M > 0$, such that if $x', z' \in S'$ and $|x' - z'| < 1/M$ then $|f'(x') - f'(z')| < 1/N$. Associated with this number $M$, there exists an index $n_0$ such that both $|x_n' - x| < 1/2M$ and $|z_n' - z| < 1/2M$ for every index $n \geq n_0$; hence,

$$|x_n' - z_n'| \leq |x_n' - x| + |x - z_n'| < \frac{1}{M}$$

for every index $n \geqslant n_0$. Thus, $|f'(x_n') - f'(z_n')| < 1/N$ when $n \geqslant n_0$, which shows that $(f'(x_n'))$ and $(f'(z_n'))$ are equivalent Cauchy sequences.

To finish the proof, we must show that $f$ is continuous on $S$. Since every point $x$ of $S$ is in some bounded part $T$ of $S$, it is enough to prove that if $T$ is any bounded part of $S$, then $f$ is uniformly continuous on $T$. This implies, indeed, that $f$ is continuous on $T$ and, therefore, at the arbitrary point $x$ of $S$. At the same time, since we have not excluded that $T = S$ whenever $S$ is assumed to be bounded, this will also prove that $f$ is uniformly continuous on $S$ when $S$ is bounded.

Thus, let us assume that $T$ is a bounded part of $S$. By the proposition on page 106, it is sufficient to show that if $(x_n)$ is any Cauchy sequence of elements of $T$, then $(f(x_n))$ is also a Cauchy sequence.

Given any natural number $N$, since $f'$ is uniformly continuous on $S'$, there exists an integer $M > 0$ such that if $x', z' \in S'$, $|x' - z'| < 1/M$ then $|f'(x') - f'(z')| < 1/3N$.

Since $(x_n)$ is a Cauchy sequence, associated with this integer $M$, there exists an index $n_0$ such that if $m, n \geqslant n_0$ then $|x_m - x_n| < 1/3M$.

Consider any two indices $m, n \geqslant n_0$. Since $x_m = \lim_{k \to \infty} x'_{m,k}$, $x_n = \lim_{k \to \infty} x'_{n,k}$, there exists a sufficiently large index $k_0$ (depending on $m, n$) such that if $k \geqslant k_0$ then $|x_m - x'_{m,k}| < 1/3M$ and also $|x_n - x'_{n,k}| < 1/3M$; therefore, if $m, n \geqslant n_0$, and taking any index $k \geqslant k_0$, we have

$$x'_{m,k} - x'_{n,k} = (x'_{m,k} - x_m) + (x_m - x_n) + (x_n - x'_{n,k}),$$

so

$$|x'_{m,k} - x'_{n,k}| < 1/M.$$

Hence, by the uniform continuity of $f'$, $|f'(x'_{m,k}) - f'(x'_{n,k})| < 1/3N$, provided $m, n \geqslant n_0$ and $k \geqslant k_0$.

On the other hand, considering any two indices $m, n \geqslant n_0$, since $f(x_m) = \lim_{k \to \infty} f'(x'_{m,k})$, $f(x_n) = \lim_{k \to \infty} f'(x'_{n,k})$, given the natural number $N$, there exists a sufficiently large index $k_1$, which we may take such that $k_1 \geqslant k_0$, with the property: if $k \geqslant k_1$ then $|f(x_m) - f'(x'_{m,k})| < 1/3N$ and $|f(x_n) - f'(x'_{n,k})| < 1/3N$. Combining these inequalities, if $m, n \geqslant n_0$, and using $k \geqslant k_1$, it follows from

$$f(x_m) - f(x_n) = (f(x_m) - f'(x'_{m,k})) + (f'(x'_{m,k}) - f'(x'_{n,k})) + (f'(x'_{n,k}) - f(x_n))$$

that

$$|f(x_m) - f(x_n)| \leq \frac{1}{3N} + \frac{1}{3N} + \frac{1}{3N} = \frac{1}{N}$$

This shows that $(f(x_n))$ is a Cauchy sequence, and concludes our proof.

## An Application of Uniform Continuity

The subject of uniform continuity, which deserves careful attention, has many applications in analysis. It is a fundamental tool in the study of power series and the definition of new continuous functions by means of these series.

Since power series will not be treated here, we re-examine the definition of powers of real numbers and show, by theoretical means, how it is possible to introduce the power $a^x$, when $a$, $x$ are real numbers, $a > 0$, avoiding as much as possible any numerical computations.

We summarize the different steps.

(a) If $q$ is a natural number, we define $a^q$ as a product of $q$ numbers equal to $a$; we define also $a^0 = 1$.

(b) If $q$ is a natural number, we define $a^{-q} = 1/a^q$ (which is possible since $a^q \neq 0$).

(c) For every fixed natural number $q > 1$, the function which associates with every real number $x > 0$ the power $x^q$ is a continuous, strictly increasing function, with range $(0, +\infty)$. Hence, it has an inverse function, which is also continuous and strictly increasing; we put $x = a^{1/q}$ exactly when $a = x^q$. Then, using (a) and (b), we may define $a^r$, where $r$ is any rational number.

(d) For every fixed real number $a > 0$ and for every bounded interval, for example $[-n, n]$, the function $r \to a^r$ is uniformly continuous on the set of all rational numbers of $[-n, n]$.

In fact, let $N$ be any natural number; since the function $r \to a^r$, defined on the rational numbers, is continuous at $r = 0$, given any natural number $N'$, there exists an integer $M > 0$, such that if $|r| < 1/M$ then $|1 - a^r| < 1/N'$. Therefore, by taking $N'$ such that $N' > a^n.N$, if $r, r'$ are rational numbers in the interval $[-n, n]$, and $|r - r'| < 1/M$ then

$$|a^r - a^{r'}| \leqslant a^r.|1 - a^{r'-r}| < a^n \cdot \frac{1}{N'} < \frac{1}{N}$$

By using the preceding extension theorem, there exists one and only one continuous function $f_n$, defined on the interval $[-n, n]$ and such that $f_n(r) = a^r$, for every rational number $r$, $-n \leq r \leq n$. Now, if $n < n'$, then the functions $f_n, f_{n'}$ coincide at every point $x$ such that $|x| \leqslant n$. Therefore, we may define a function $f$, on the whole real line, as follows: if $x$ is any real number, if $n$ is an integer, $|x| \leqslant n$, we write $f(x) = f_n(x)$; this definition is independent of the integer $n$.

This unique function $f$, thus obtained, is called the EXPONENTIAL FUNC-TION WITH BASIS $a > 0$, and we denote $f(x) = a^x$ for every real number $x$.

As an exercise, establish a proof for the main properties of the exponential function.

PROPOSITION. *If a is a real number, a > 0, then:*

(1) $a^{x+y} = a^x.a^y$, $(a^x)^y = a^{x \cdot y}$, *where x, y are any real numbers.*

(2) *The range of the exponential function (with basis $a \neq 1$) is the open half line $(0, +\infty)$.*

(3) *The function $a^x$, with $a > 1$, is strictly increasing, and with $a < 1$, it is strictly decreasing; with $a = 1$, the function is constant equal to 1.*

(4) *If $a > 1$ then $\lim\limits_{x \to +\infty} a^x = +\infty$, $\lim\limits_{x \to -\infty} a^x = 0$; if $0 < a < 1$ then $\lim\limits_{x \to +\infty} a^x = 0$, $\lim\limits_{x \to -\infty} a^x = +\infty$.*

From our theory, we know that each exponential function (with basis $a \neq 1$) has a continuous inverse function, which will be called the LOGARITHMIC FUNCTION WITH BASIS $a > 0$, $a \neq 1$. We denote by $\log_a x$ the value of this function at the real number $x$.

Thus, $\log_a(a^x) = x$ and $a^{\log_a x} = x$, for every $x > 0$.

The formulas below may be proved as an exercise:

$$\log_a (x.y) = \log_a x + \log_a y, \quad \log_a (x^\alpha) = \alpha.\log_a x,$$

where $x, y > 0$ and $\alpha$ is any real number.

Each logarithmic function, with $a > 1$, is strictly increasing while, with $0 < a < 1$, it is strictly decreasing. They are defined on the halfline $(0, +\infty)$, with range of values equal to the whole real line. Their graphs are symmetric, (with respect to the bisector of the angle of the coordinate axes) to the graphs (Figures 13, 14) of the corresponding exponential functions (see page 68).

If $a > 1$ then $\lim\limits_{x \to +\infty} \log_a x = +\infty$, $\lim\limits_{x \to 0} \log_a x = -\infty$.

If $0 < a < 1$ then $\lim\limits_{x \to +\infty} \log_a x = -\infty$, $\lim\limits_{x \to 0} \log_a x = +\infty$.

The graphs of these functions are shown in Figures 13 and 14.

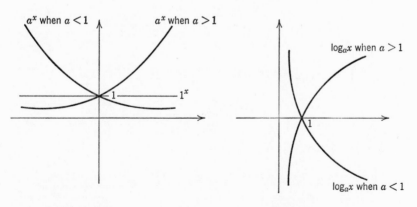

Figure 13          Figure 14

From the above considerations, we see that for different values of $a \neq 1$, these functions have a graph of the same shape, and play a similar role. This may be deduced from the following relations between exponential and logarithmic functions, for different bases.

If $a$, $b$ are strictly positive real numbers, distinct from 1, then $b^x = a^{x \cdot \log_a b}$, where $x$ is any real number, and $\log_b x = \log_b a \cdot \log_a x$, where $x > 0$.

In practice, it is common to choose among the exponential and logarithmic functions, the ones with a basis equal to the number $e$ discussed on page 57. There are many reasons for the outstanding role of the number $e$ in this connection, which may be easily explained by the use of integrals. Since the subject of integrals is beyond the scope of this book, we shall not go into this explanation here. Instead, we shall derive, by purely elementary means, without using the notions of derivatives or integrals, a certain property of the number $e$, which gives a special place to the exponential function $e^x$ among all the exponential functions $a^x$.

### Characterization of the Number e

Generalizing a result established on page 55:

*If* $1 + k > 0$ *then* $(1 + k)^x \geqslant 1 + k.x$, *for every real number* $x \geqslant 1$.

Of course, we may take $x > 1$. We first prove the result for the case of a rational number $r > 1$.

Let $r = p/q > 1$, with $p, q$ natural integers, $p > q$. Since the function $a \to a^q$, for $a > 0$, is strictly increasing, it is enough to prove that $(1 + k)^p \geqslant [1 + (p/q)k]^q$. This may be achieved by a direct computation, using the NEWTON binomial formula

$$(1 + k)^p = 1 + p.k + \frac{p(p - 1)}{2!} k^2 + \ldots$$

$$+ \frac{p(p - 1) \ldots (p - n + 1)}{n!} k^n + \ldots + k^p$$

$$\left(1 + \frac{p}{q} k\right)^q = 1 + q \cdot \frac{p}{q} k + \frac{q(q - 1)}{2!} \frac{p^2}{q^2} k^2 + \ldots$$

$$+ \frac{q(q - 1) \ldots (q - n + 1)}{n!} \frac{p^n}{q^n} k^n + \ldots + \frac{p^q}{q^q} k^q.$$

From $p > q$, it follows that for every index $n \leqslant q < p$, we have

$$\frac{p(p - 1) \ldots (p - n + 1)}{n!} k^n > \frac{q(q - 1) \ldots (q - n + 1)}{n!} \frac{p^n}{q^n} k^n$$

since this is equivalent to

$$\left(1-\frac{1}{p}\right)\left(1-\frac{2}{p}\right)\cdots\left(1-\frac{n-1}{p}\right) > \left(1-\frac{1}{q}\right)\left(1-\frac{2}{q}\right)$$
$$\cdots\left(1-\frac{n-1}{q}\right)$$

For $q < n \leqslant p$ there are only positive terms in $(1+k)^p$ and no terms in $[1+(p/q)k]^q$.

Now, if $x > 1$ is any irrational number, then there exists a sequence of rational numbers $(r_n)$, $r_n > 1$, such that $\lim r_n = x$. By definition of the powers, $(1+k)^x = \lim_{n\to\infty}(1+k)^{r_n} \geqslant \lim_{n\to\infty}(1+r_n.k) = 1+x.k$.

This proves our assertion.

Now, we shall consider, for every $a > 1$, the function $y = a^x$, defined for every real number $x > 0$, and we shall compare it with the function $y = x + 1$.

Let $S$ be the set of all real numbers $a > 1$ for which $a^x > 1 + x$, for every $x > 0$.

(a) The set $S$ is nonempty.

Indeed, 3 is in $S$. This follows from the computation on page 57, where we have shown that $3 > (1+1/n)^n$, for every natural number $n$. Therefore, given a real number $x > 0$, and choosing $n$ so large that $n.x > 1$, by the above lemma,

$$3^x > \left(1+\frac{1}{n}\right)^{nx} \geqslant 1+\frac{nx}{n} = 1+x.$$

This being true for every $x > 0$, it follows that 3 is in $S$.

(b) Clearly, if $a \in S$ and $a < b$ then also $b \in S$.

(c) On the other hand, for every natural number $m$, $(1+1/m)^m$ is not in $S$.

Indeed, let $x$ be such that $0 < x < 1/m$; then

$$(1+x)^{1/mx} \geqslant 1+\frac{x}{mx} = 1+\frac{1}{m}$$

hence

$$1+x \geqslant \left(1+\frac{1}{m}\right)^{mx}.$$

(d) Moreover, if $a$ is not in $S$, if $x$ is such that $a^x \leqslant 1+x$, if $0 < x' < x$, then $a^{x'} \leqslant 1+x'$.

Because, from

$$a^{x'} > 1+x', \quad x = \frac{x}{x'}.x', \quad \frac{x}{x'} > 1,$$

we deduce that

$$a^x = (a^{x'})^{x/x'} > (1 + x')^{x/x'} \geqslant 1 + x' \cdot \frac{x}{x'} = 1 + x$$

This is the contrapositive of our assertion.

(e) Consider now the greatest lower bound of the set $S$ which, temporarily, we shall call, $s$. We have seen that $(1 + 1/m)^m \leqslant s$, for every natural number $m$, and also $s \leqslant 3$.

(f) We show that $s$ is in the set $S$.

It is enough to verify that if $a$ is not in $S$, there exists a sufficiently large integer $n$ such that $a + 1/n$ is still not in $S$.

Let $x > 0$ be such that $a^x \leqslant 1 + x$. Choosing an integer $m$ such that $1/(m + 1) < x$, then $a^{1/m+1} \leqslant 1 + 1/(m + 1)$ as follows from (d). Thus

$$a \leqslant \left(1 + \frac{1}{m+1}\right)^{m+1} < \left(1 + \frac{1}{m}\right)^m$$

by the computation on page 57; hence there exists an integer $n > 0$ such that $a + 1/n < (1 + 1/m)^m$ and, thus, it follows from (c) and (b) that $a + 1/n$ is not in $S$.

(g) In (f), we have also proved that, given any natural number $N$, there exists some natural number $m$ such that

$$s - \frac{1}{N} < \left(1 + \frac{1}{m}\right)^m$$

We only need to take $a = s - 1/N$, which is not in $S$.

Since the sequence with the general term $(1 + 1/m)^m$ is increasing, it follows that $s = \lim_{m \to \infty} (1 + 1/m)^m$.

Thus, we have shown that $s$ is exactly the number $e$, previously defined as the above limit.

Summarizing, we have proved the following.

*The number $e$ is the smallest real number with the property $e^x > 1 + x$, for every real number $x > 0$.*

### Exercises

1. Write explicitly the negation of the statement of uniform continuity.

2. Show that the function $y = +\sqrt{x}$ is uniformly continuous in the half-line $[1, +\infty)$. Explicitly, given $\epsilon > 0$, determine $\delta > 0$, independent of $x$, such that if $|x_1 - x_2| < \delta$, with $x_1, x_2 \in [1, +\infty)$, then $|\sqrt{x_1} - \sqrt{x_2}| < \epsilon$.

3. Show that if $f$, $g$ are two uniformly continuous functions on the interval $[a, b]$, then the function $f.g$ is also uniformly continuous on $[a, b]$.

4. Prove Cantor's *nested interval theorem:* if $(I_n)$ is a sequence of closed intervals, each being contained in the preceding one, there exists a real number common to all the intervals $I_n$.

5. Let $C$ be a nonempty collection of closed intervals, with the following *finite intersection property:* if $I_1, \ldots, I_n$ are any finite number of intervals in $C$, they have a point in common.

Show that there exists a point belonging to all the intervals of the collection $C$.

*Hint.* Consider an interval $I_1$ of the collection; for every interval $I$ of $C$, $I \neq I_1$, consider the *complementary set*, that is, the one formed by all the real numbers not belonging to $I$; it is a union of open intervals: let $C'$ be the collection of all open intervals thus obtained; show that $C'$ is an open covering of the closed interval $I_1$; apply Heine-Borel theorem and the finite intersection property to conclude the proof.

6. Give an example of an infinite sequence of sets $S_n$ of real numbers, which constitute a covering of the open interval $(0, 1)$, in such a way that no finite collection of the sets $S_n$ will cover $(0, 1)$.

7. Check the details of the following alternative proof of Heine-Borel theorem.

Assume the closed interval $[a, b]$ covered by the collection $C$ of open intervals. Let $S$ be the set of all real numbers $x$ in $[a, b]$ such that the closed interval $[a, x]$ may be covered by a finite number of the intervals belonging to the given collection $C$. The set $S$ is nonempty. If $x \in S$ and $a < x' < x$, then $x' \in S$. $S$ is bounded above, therefore it has a least upper bound $s$. If $s = b$ then the theorem is true. If $s < b$, let $I$ be an open interval in the collection $C$ containing $s$; let $s' \in S$, $s' \in I$, $s' < s$. There exist intervals $I_1, \ldots, I_m$, belonging to $C$, which cover $[a, s']$; hence $I_1, \ldots, I_m, I$ cover $[a, s]$ as well as any interval $[a, s'']$, where $s < s'' < b$, $s'' \in I$. Then $s'' \in S$, which is a contradiction.

8. Check the proof of the following theorem, discovered by LINDELÖF.

Let $S$ be any set of real numbers, covered by a collection $C$ of open intervals. Then, it is possible to select from this collection $C$, a sequence of intervals $I_1, I_2, \ldots, I_m, \ldots$ (not necessarily distinct), which constitute still a covering of $S$.

*Proof.* Consider the collection $C'$ of all intervals of type $(r - 1/n, r + 1/n)$, where $r$ is a rational number of $S$ and $n$ a natural number; by the results in

Appendix B, the set of rational numbers is countable and so is the collection $C'$ above; therefore, the intervals of the collection $C'$ may be written in a sequence $I'_1, I'_2, \ldots, I'_n, \ldots$. Let $I_0$ be any one fixed interval belonging to the collection $C$. With every interval $I_n'$ of $C'$, we associate some interval $I_n$ of the collection $C$, as follows: if no interval of $C$ contains $I'_n$, we associate with $I_n'$ the fixed interval $I_0$; if some interval of $C$ contains $I'_n$, we choose in any way one among those containing $I'_n$. In both cases, we denote by $I_n$ the chosen interval of $C$. The sequence $I_1, I_2, \ldots, I_n, \ldots$ of (not necessarily distinct) intervals belonging to $C$ constitute a covering of $S$; complete the proof of this last assertion.

9. Check the details of the following alternative proof of the Heine-Borel theorem.

Using Lindelöf's theorem, it is possible to replace the given covering $C$ by another one which is a sequence of (not necessarily distinct) open intervals $I_1, I_2, \ldots, I_n, \ldots$. Assume that it is possible to find, for every index $n$, an element $x_n$ which is in $I_n$, in $[a, b]$, but which is not in any of the preceding intervals $I_1, \ldots, I_{n-1}$. The infinite set $\{x_n\}$ is bounded, hence it has an accumulation point $s$, $a \leqslant s \leqslant b$. There exists an interval $I_m$ such that $s \in I_m$ and, necessarily, infinitely many terms of the sequence $x_n$ are in $I_m$; at any rate, some $x_n \in I_m$, with $n > m$, which is a contradiction. Hence, already a finite number of the intervals $I_i$ cover $[a, b]$.

10. Prove statements (1) and (2) on page 99, by establishing that each of the following properties for a set $S$ implies the other ones.

(a) $S$ is a compact set.

(b) $S$ is closed and bounded.

(c) From any given sequence $(a_n)$ of numbers of $S$, it is possible to extract a convergent subsequence $(a_{n_k})_k$, whose limit is in $S$ (then $S$ is called a SEQUENTIALLY COMPACT SET).

*Hint.* Show, first, that if $S$ is compact, then it is bounded and closed.

$S$ is bounded, since given the open covering of $S$ formed by all the intervals $(-n, n)$, where $n$ is any integer, it is possible to select a finite number of intervals which still cover $S$.

To prove that $S$ is closed, let $(x_n)$ be a convergent sequence of elements of $S$ and assume that its limit $x_0$ does not belong to $S$. Since $S$ is bounded, it is contained in some open interval $(a, b)$, with $a < x_0 < b$. The collection of intervals of type $(a, x_0 - 1/n)$, $(x_0 + 1/n, b)$, where $n$ is any natural number, form an open covering of $S$; therefore, there exists a finite number of these intervals which already cover $S$; check that this contradicts the hypothesis that $x_0 = \lim x_n$, $x_n \in S$.

Next, assume that $S$ is a bounded and closed set. Use the result on page 47 to deduce the assertion (c).

Finally, assume that $S$ is a set satisfying the condition (c). Consider an open covering of $S$ by a collection $\mathcal{C}$ of open intervals. By Lindelöf's theorem (Exercise 8), there exists a sequence $I_1, \ldots, I_n, \ldots$, of intervals belonging to $\mathcal{C}$, which still forms a covering of $S$. As in the previous exercise, if no finite collection of intervals may be selected to cover $S$, it is possible to construct a sequence $(x_n)$ of elements of $S$, each $x_n$ being in $I_n$, but not in any of the previous intervals $I_1, \ldots, I_{n-1}$. Then, conclude the proof as in the previous exercise.

# Appendix A

# Other Methods For Defining Real Numbers

We have presented in the text the definition of real numbers by CANTOR. DEDEKIND also constructed the real numbers at about the same time, and in an independent way.

Clearly, Dedekind's, Cantor's, or any other method of construction must produce the same mathematical objects, that is, the real numbers.

This appendix is divided into two parts: the first devoted to Dedekind's construction, and the second to the axiomatic definition of the real number system.

## PART I. DEDEKIND'S Construction of the Real Numbers

Our starting point is, again, the set of rational numbers, whose properties will be freely used without any further reference. We should ignore, for a while, everything discussed in Chapter 3, and start anew to build the system of real numbers. Of course, no property of the real numbers should be used here. Our treatment will be as follows.

(1) We shall define the "cuts" or "upper classes" of rational numbers.

(2) We shall introduce operations and inequalities with such upper classes.

(3) We shall show that there is no mathematical reason to distinguish between the set of real numbers and the set of upper classes of rational numbers, with respect to its operations and inequalities.

This means that it will be possible to find a one-to-one correspondence from the set of real numbers onto the set of upper classes of rational numbers, in such a way that sums correspond to sums, products to products, and so on. When this is the case, we say that the two mathematical systems are ISOMORPHIC; they may only be distinguished by notation, or by the nature of their elements, but not at all by mathematical operations making sense in these systems.

We warn that it is not our intention to carry out the details of this construction. This would be lengthy and not very instructive. The important thing, here, is to make clear the possibility of defining real numbers in different equivalent ways, and to state the main steps in the construction. A good test of understanding would be to provide all the details of the proofs as an exercise.

A CUT or UPPER CLASS in the set of rational numbers is a set $U$ of rational numbers having the following properties.*

(1)  $U$ is not empty.

(2)  Some rational number is not in $U$.

(3)  If a rational number $r \in U$ and $s$ is a rational number such that $r < s$, then $s \in U$.

(4)  $U$ does not contain a rational number $r_0$ with the property that $r_0 \leqslant r$, for every $r \in U$ (that is, $U$ has no smallest element).

Two upper classes $U$, $U'$ are *equal* when every element of $U$ is in $U'$, and vice versa; that is, the sets $U$, $U'$ are equal.

We say that $U$ *is less or equal to* $U'$, and write $U \leqslant U'$ when every rational number belonging to $U'$ is also in $U$; that means that the set $U'$ is a part of $U$. In case $U \leqslant U'$, but $U \neq U'$, we write $U < U'$, and say that $U$ is strictly smaller than $U'$. Thus, given any two upper classes $U, U'$, either $U < U'$, or $U = U'$, or $U' < U$.

Every rational number $r_0$ defines an upper class $U(r_0)$, which is the set of all rational numbers $r$ such that $r > r_0$ (check that property (4) is verified).

If $r_0$, $r_1$ are two distinct rational numbers, for example $r_0 < r_1$, then $U(r_0) < U(r_1)$. Therefore, the correspondence that associates with each rational number $r$ the upper class $U(r)$ is one-to-one and respects the inequalities.

The operations with upper classes are easily defined.

If $U$, $U'$ are upper classes, then the set of all rational numbers of type $r + r'$ (taking $r$ in $U$, $r'$ in $U'$) is an upper class of rational numbers; it is denoted by $U + U'$.

In the same way it is defined the upper class $U \cdot U'$.

To define the upper class $U - U'$, we first define $-U'$, and then say that $U - U' = U + (-U')$. Clearly, $-U'$ is *not* the set of all rational numbers of the form $-r$, taking $r$ in $U$; this would not be an upper class

---

* It should be emphasized that our definition of cut is presented in a way slightly different from the one given originally by Dedekind.

but, instead, what one might call a "lower class." The correct definition of $-U'$ is the set of all rational numbers $r$ with the property that $r + r' > 0$, whatever be the rational number $r' \in U'$.

Similarly, if $U$ is an upper class such that $U > U(0)$ (set of all rational numbers $r$ such that $r > 0$), then $U^{-1}$ is defined as the set of all rational numbers $r'$ such that $r' \cdot r > 1$, for every rational number $r \in U$. If $U$ is an upper class, $U \neq U(0)$ and $U < U(0)$, then $-U > U(0)$ and $U^{-1}$ is defined as $-(-U)^{-1}$.

It is easy to verify that, if $r_1$, $r_2$ are rational numbers, then

$$U(r_1 + r_2) = U(r_1) + U(r_2), \quad U(r_1 r_2) = U(r_1) \cdot U(r_2),$$
$$U(r_1 - r_2) = U(r_1) - U(r_2)$$

and, finally, if $r_2 \neq 0$, then

$$U(r_1/r_2) = \frac{U(r_1)}{U(r_2)} = U(r_1) \cdot U(r_2)^{-1}.$$

Thus, the operations with upper classes, when restricted to the upper classes that are defined by rational numbers, coincide with the corresponding operations of rational numbers. This is why we say that the system of rational numbers (with its operations and inequality) is contained in the system of upper classes (with its operations and inequalities).

Now, we compare the system of upper classes of rational numbers with the system of real numbers, given by Cantor's construction, as it was developed in Chapter 3.

Our purpose is to associate by a one-to-one correspondence an upper class with every given real number. This is easily done in a natural way.

Given the real number $\alpha$, let us associate with $\alpha$ the upper class $U(\alpha)$, equal to the set of all rational numbers $r$ such that $r > \alpha$ (check that $U(\alpha)$ verifies property (4) of the definition of upper class).

If $\alpha$, $\beta$ are real numbers and $\alpha < \beta$ then, as we have seen, there exists a rational number $r$ such that $\alpha < r < \beta$; hence $r \in U(\alpha)$, but $r \notin U(\beta)$, consequently $U(\alpha) < U(\beta)$. Thus, the correspondence is one-to-one, and preserves the inequalities.

We still must show that the correspondence is *onto* the set of all upper classes of rational numbers; that is, given any upper class $U$, there exists a real number $\alpha$ such that $U(\alpha) = U$. We shall prove this explicitly, as an example and because it is not so immediate as the other verifications, which we suggested as an exercise.

*Given $U$, for every natural number $n$, there exist rational numbers $a_n$, $b_n$ such that $a_n \in U$, $b_n \notin U$, $a_n > b_n$ and $a_n - b_n < 1/n$.*

Indeed, we start with any rational number $r$ in $U$, and consider all the rational numbers $r, r - 1/(n+1), r - 2/(n+1), \ldots, r - k/(n+1), \ldots$. Certainly, there exists some integer $k$ such that $r - k/(n+1) \notin U$. Otherwise, the upper class $U$ would have rational numbers, as small as we like, because of the Archimedean property of rational numbers; then $U$ would contain *all* the rational numbers, which is impossible.

Taking the smallest $k \geqslant 1$ for which $r - k/(n + 1) \notin U$, letting

$$a_n = \frac{r - k - 1}{n + 1}, \quad b_n = \frac{r - k}{n + 1},$$

then $a_n > b_n$ and $a_n - b_n = 1/(n + 1) < 1/n$.

This being established, the sequence of rational numbers $(a_n)$ (using the above numbers $a_n$) is a CAUCHY sequence. In fact, given any natural number $N$, let $n_0 = 2N$; for any integers $m, n \geqslant n_0$, let $a_m, b_m, a_n, b_n$ be determined as above, and let $b$ be the largest of the rational numbers $b_m$, $b_n$; since $b \notin U$, then $a_m > b$, $a_n > b$. Then

$$|a_m - a_n| = |(a_m - b) + (b - a_n)| \leqslant |a_m - b| + |b - a_n|$$
$$\leqslant |a_m - b_m| + |a_n - b_m| < \frac{1}{2N} + \frac{1}{2N} = \frac{1}{N}.$$

Thus, the sequence $(a_n)$ is indeed a Cauchy sequence of rational numbers. By Cantor's construction, it defines a real number $\alpha$, and our purpose is to show that the given upper class $U$ is equal to $U(\alpha)$ (the upper class that is associated to $\alpha$ by our correspondence).

We show that every rational number $r$ in $U(\alpha)$ must belong to $U$. If $r > \alpha$, let $N$ be a natural number so large that $1/N < r - \alpha$; then, there exists an index $n_0$ such that if $n \geqslant n_0$ we have

$$a_n - \alpha \leqslant |a_n - \alpha| < \frac{1}{N} < r - \alpha$$

(by the proposition on page 24). Hence $a_n < r$ and $r \in U$.

It follows that since each $b_n \notin U$ then also $b_n \notin U(\alpha)$, that is, $b_n \leqslant \alpha$.

Now we prove that every element $r \in U$ is also in $U(\alpha)$. If we have some $r \in U$, $r < \alpha$, then every $b_n < r$ (otherwise, some $n_1$ exists for which $r \leqslant b_{n_1}$, hence $b_{n_1} \in U$, because $r \in U$; this is impossible). Letting $N$ be a natural number, so large that $1/N < \alpha - r$, and $n_0$ be an index such that if $n \geqslant n_0$ then $|\alpha - a_n| < 1/2N$, by taking also $n \geqslant 2N$, we have $a_n - b_n < 1/n \leqslant 1/2N$. Therefore, for such large index $n$, we have

$$r - b_n = (\alpha - a_n) + (a_n - b_n) - (\alpha - r)$$
$$\leqslant |\alpha - a_n| + (a_n - b_n) - (\alpha - r) < \frac{1}{2N} + \frac{1}{2N} - \frac{1}{N} = 0,$$

a contradiction.

This shows that if $r \in U$, it is impossible that $r < \alpha$. Therefore, it is also impossible that $r = \alpha$, for then it would be the smallest element of $U$, contrary to condition (4) of the definition of upper class. Thus, the only possibility left is that $r > \alpha$.

The proof is therefore concluded.

Next, we note that the above correspondence $\alpha \rightarrow U(\alpha)$ preserves the operations and inequalities.

$$U(\alpha + \beta) = U(\alpha) + U(\beta)$$
$$U(\alpha \cdot \beta) = U(\alpha) \cdot U(\beta), \text{ etc., and}$$
$$\alpha < \beta \text{ if and only if } U(\alpha) < U(\beta).$$

These proofs are straightforward.

These considerations enable us to identify the collection of upper classes of rational numbers (with its operations and inequality) with the system of real numbers.

A repetition of Dedekind's process, using the collection of upper classes of *real* numbers, does not yield any larger system of numbers. As an exercise, develop explicitly the following considerations.

(a) Define the notion of an upper class $\mathcal{U}$ in the collection $\mathcal{C}$ of upper classes of rational numbers.

(b) Show that for every upper class $\mathcal{U}$ in the collection $\mathcal{C}$ of upper classes of rational numbers there exists an upper class $U_0$ belonging to $\mathcal{C}$, such that $\mathcal{U}$ is exactly the set of all upper classes $U$ of $\mathcal{C}$ such that $U > U_0$.

The significance of this conclusion is the same as that of the Cauchy convergence criterion.

## PART II. The Axiomatic Definition of the Real Numbers

As may have been noticed, very often we are more concerned with operational properties of the objects to be studied than with their intrinsic nature.

In other words, to define new mathematical entities, we use constructions based on already known objects, such as the real numbers, which are defined by means of the rational numbers, and these by means of the integers.

We are then interested in establishing the operational laws with the new symbols; in the uses of these symbols, quite often what is directly needed are these laws of operation.

Therefore, it is a good idea to study mathematical systems with regard to the laws of operations with their symbols.

Our treatment in this part will be as follows.

(1) We shall give a list of properties satisfied by the real numbers, concerning operations of addition, multiplication, and inequalities.

(2) The above list will be "complete": that is, it will contain enough properties to allow us to derive by purely logical arguments *any other* property of the real numbers.

(3) The above list will be "economical"; that is, by deleting any one of the properties on the list, the reduced list will no longer be complete in the sense of (2).

The following question arises naturally.

How can we know that a list of properties is complete? Certainly not by trying to determine whether every single property of the real numbers can be deduced logically from the ones in the list. First, there are infinitely many properties of real numbers, and we cannot expect to check, one after the other, whether they may be logically deduced from the ones given in the list. It might also be that a property is logically deductible from those in our list, but we are unable to do so.

There is, however, a way of verifying that a list of properties of the real number system is complete.

We consider an *abstract* mathematical system $S$, whose elements are symbols, among which operations are defined so as to satisfy exactly the properties in the given list; we say that these properties are the AXIOMS of the mathematical system $S$.

Then, we attempt to define a one-to-one correspondence from the set $S$ onto the set $R$ of real numbers in such a way that the operations and inequalities are preserved. If this is achieved, it means that, except for notation or presentation, there is no mathematical reason to distinguish between the systems $R$ of real numbers and $S$ of symbols, with the properties in the given list. Therefore, every property of one system is shared by the other one. Since those properties of $S$ are necessarily established by logical arguments, nothing being said about the nature of the elements of $S$, it means that the given list of properties of $R$ is complete.

### Axioms for the System of Real Numbers

Let $S$ be a set of elements, on which operations $+$, $\cdot$ are defined, and a relation $\leqslant$ is defined. We assume that the properties listed below are satisfied.

*I. Properties of $+$*

(1) If $a$, $b \in S$ there exists a uniquely defined element in $S$, denoted by $a + b$ (the operation $+$ is always defined).

(2) If $a, b, c \in S$ then $a + (b + c) = (a + b) + c$ (associative law).

(3) If $a, b \in S$ then $a + b = b + a$ (commutative law).

(4) There exists an element in $S$, denoted $z$, such that $a + z = a$, for every $a \in S$.

(5) For every element $a \in S$ there exists an element in $S$, denoted $-a$, called the *symmetric of a*, such that $a + (-a) = z$.

## II. *Properties of* ·

(1) If $a, b \in S$ there exists a uniquely defined element in $S$, denoted by $ab$ (the operation · is always defined).

(2) If $a, b, c \in S$ then $a(bc) = (ab)c$ (associative law).

(3) If $a, b \in S$ then $ab = ba$ (commutative law).

(4) There exists an element in $S$, denoted $e$, such that $e \neq z$, $ae = a$ for every $a \in S$.

(5) For every element $a \in S$, $a \neq z$, there exists an element in $S$, denoted $a^{-1}$, called the *inverse of a*, such that $aa^{-1} = e$.

## III. *Property of* + *and* ·

(1) If $a, b, c \in S$ then $a(b + c) = ab + ac$ (distributive law).

## IV. *Properties of* $\leqslant$

(1) If $a \in S$ then $a \leqslant a$ (reflexive property).

(2) If $a, b \in S$ and $a \leqslant b$, $b \leqslant a$, then $a = b$ (antisymmetric property).

(3) If $a, b, c \in S$ and $a \leqslant b$, $b \leqslant c$, then $a \leqslant c$ (transitive property).

(4) If $a, b \in S$ then either $a \leqslant b$ or $b \leqslant a$ (linear property).

## V. *Properties of* $\leqslant$, +, ·

(1) If $a, b \in S$ and $z \leqslant a$, $z \leqslant b$ then $z \leqslant a + b$ (compatibility with +).

(2) If $a, b \in S$ and $z \leqslant a$, $z \leqslant b$, then $z \leqslant ab$ (compatibility with ·).

## VI. *Completeness property*

Let $S'$ be a nonempty part of $S$ such that there exists an element $a \in S$ with the property $b < a$, for every element $b \in S'$. Then, there exists an element $u \in S$ with the following properties.

(a) If $b \in S'$ then $b \leqslant u$.

(b) If $u' \in S$ is such that $b \leqslant u'$ for every element $b \in S'$, then $u \leqslant u'$.

Introducing an obvious terminology, we may phrase this last axiom as follows: every nonempty collection of elements in $S$, which is bounded above, has a least upper bound.

A mathematical system $S$ with the above axioms is called a COMPLETE ORDERED FIELD. It is a *field*, which means that it satisfies axioms I, II, and III; it is an *ordered field*, meaning that it satisfies also axioms IV and V; and, finally, it is *complete*, which accounts for axiom VI.

As we know from the text, the system of real numbers is an example of a complete ordered field, where 0 has the role of $z$, and 1 has the role of $e$.

As a challenging task, provide proofs by means of logical deduction, of the following properties of a complete ordered field. At every step, it is only permissible to use the given axioms and the already proved statements.

(1) There exists only one element in $S$, that is, $z$, sharing the same property: $a + z = a$ for every $a \in S$.

(2) For every element $a \in S$, there exists only one element in $S$, that is, $-a$, sharing the same property: $a + (-a) = z$.

(3) $-z = z$.

(4) For every element $a \in S$, we have $-(-a) = a$.

(5) If $a, b \in S$ then $-(a + b) = (-a) + (-b)$.

(6) If $a, b, c \in S$ and $a + b = a + c$ then $b = c$.

(7) Define *subtraction of elements in* $S$ as follows: $a - b = a + (-b)$. Show that $a - (b - c) = (a - b) + c$, where $a, b, c \in S$.

(8) There exists only one element in $S$, that is, $e$, sharing the same property: $a.e = a$, for every $a \in S$.

(9) For every element $a \in S$, $a \neq z$, there exists only one element in $S$, that is, $a^{-1}$, sharing the same property: $a.a^{-1} = e$.

(10) $e^{-1} = e$.

(11) If $a \in S$, $a \neq z$, then $a^{-1} \neq z$ and $(a^{-1})^{-1} = a$.

(12) If $a \in S$ then $a.z = z$.

(13) There exists no element $a \in S$ such that $a.z = e$.

(14) If $a, b \in S$, $a \neq z$, $b \neq z$, then $ab \neq z$.

(15) If $a, b \in S$, $a \neq z$, $b \neq z$, then $(ab)^{-1} = a^{-1}b^{-1}$.

(16) If $a, b, c \in S$, $a \neq z$, and $ab = ac$, then $b = c$.

(17) $(-e).(-e) = e$.

(18) If $a \in S$ then $(-e).a = -a$.

(19) If $a, b \in S$ then $(-a).b = a.(-b) = -(a.b)$.

(20) If $a, b \in S$ then $(-a).(-b) = ab$.

(21) Define *division of* $a \in S$ *by* $b \in S$, where $b \neq z$, as follows: $a/b = a.b^{-1}$. Prove that if $a \in S$ then $a^{-1} = e/a$; if $a, b, d \in S$, $b \neq z$, $d \neq z$, then $a/b = ad/bd$.

(22) If $a, b, c, d \in S$ and $b \neq z, d \neq z$, then

$$\frac{a}{b} + \frac{c}{d} = \frac{ad + bc}{bd}.$$

(23) If $a, b, c, d \in S$ and $b \neq z, d \neq z$, then

$$\frac{a}{b} \cdot \frac{c}{d} = \frac{ac}{bd}.$$

(24) If $a, b \in S$, $b \neq z$, then

$$-\frac{a}{b} = \frac{-a}{b} = \frac{a}{-b}.$$

(25) If $a, b, c \in S$ then $a(b - c) = ab - ac$.

(26) If $a, b, c, d \in S$ then

$$(a + b) \cdot (c + d) = (ac + bd) + (ad + bc),$$
$$(a - b) \cdot (c - d) = (ac + bd) - (ad + bc).$$

(27) If $a, b, c, d \in S$ then

$$a - b = c - d \text{ if and only if } a + d = b + c.$$

(28) Define, for every integer $n \geqslant 2$,

$$a_1 + a_2 + \ldots + a_n = (a_1 + \ldots + a_{n-1}) + a_n,$$

where every $a_1 \in S$. Prove, by the principle of finite induction, the general associative-commutative law for the operation $+$: if $a_1, \ldots, a_n \in S$ then $a_1 + a_2 + \ldots + a_n$ is the only element obtained from the above elements by the operation $+$, whatever be their grouping by parentheses and their order; for example,

$$(a_1 + a_2) + (a_3 + a_4) = (a_1 + a_3) + (a_2 + a_4) = a_3 + (a_2 + (a_1 + a_4))$$
$$= \ldots = a_1 + a_2 + a_3 + a_4.$$

(29) Similar results holds for the operation $\cdot$.

(30) If $a \in S$ then $a \geqslant z$ if and only if $z \geqslant -a$.

(31) If $a \in S$ then $a^2 = a.a \geqslant z$.

(32) $e > z$ (that is, $e \geqslant z$, but $e \neq z$).

(33) No element $a \in S$ exists such that $a^2 = -e$.

(34) If $a, b \in S$ and $a^2 + b^2 = z$ then $a = b = z$.

(35) The correspondence that associates to every natural number $n$ the element $e + e + \ldots + e$ ($n$ times) of $S$ is one-to-one, that is: $e + e + \ldots + e \neq z$ always. Denoting $ne = e + e + \ldots + e$ ($n$ times), we have: $ne + me = (n + m)e$, $(ne).(me) = (nm)e$ and $n < m$ if and only if $ne < me$. Defining $(-n)e = -(ne)$, when $n$ is a natural number, this correspondence allows us to identify the set of integers, with its operations and inequality, with the part of $S$ composed of elements of type $ne$. Thus, we may say that $S$ contains the set of integers as a subsystem.

(36) For every $a \in S$ and natural number $n$, we denote $na = a + a + \ldots + a$ ($n$ times). Define also $(-n)a = -(na)$, for every natural number $n$. Then $0a = z$, $na = (ne)a$, $(na).(mb) = (nm)(ab)$, for any integers $n, m$. Defining

$$\frac{n}{m}e = \frac{ne}{me},$$

where $n$, $m$ are integers, $m \neq 0$, we have

$$\frac{n}{m} e + \frac{n'}{m'} e = \left(\frac{n}{m} + \frac{n'}{m'}\right) e$$

$$\frac{n}{m} e \cdot \frac{n'}{m'} e = \left(\frac{n}{m} \cdot \frac{n'}{m'}\right) e$$

$$\frac{n}{m} e < \frac{n'}{m'} e \quad \text{if and only if} \quad \frac{n}{m} < \frac{n'}{m'} \quad \text{(using } m, m' \neq 0\text{)}.$$

Thus, we may say that $S$ contains the set of rational numbers, with its operations and inequality, as a subsystem.

Therefore, it is justifiable to denote

$$\frac{n}{m} e = \frac{ne}{me}$$

as $n/m$ (where $n$, $m$ are integers, $m \neq 0$).

Now we state the following main result.

(37) *If S is a complete ordered field, there exists a one-to-one correspondence, preserving operations and inequalities, from the set S onto the system of real numbers.*

We indicate here the main steps of the proof, sometimes omitting the details.

(38) Archimedean property: if $a, b \in S$, $a > z$, there exists a natural number $n$ such that $na \geqslant b$.

Assume that $b > na$ for every natural number $n$; we shall obtain a contradiction. This means that the set $a, 2a, 3a, \ldots, na, \ldots$ is bounded above by the element $b$. By axiom VI, there exists an element $u \in S$ such that $na \leqslant u$ for every natural number $n$; however, since $u - a < u$, there exists a natural number $n_0$ such that $u - a < n_0 a$. Hence, $u < a + n_0 a = (n_0 + 1)a$, which is a contradiction.

(39) If $a \in S$, $a > z$, there exists a natural number $n$ such that $z < e/ne < a$.

Indeed, since $z < a$, there exists a natural number $n$ such that $e < na = (ne)a$, and this means that $z < e/ne < a$.

(40) Every element $a \in S$ is the least upper bound of the set of all elements $me/ne$ which are such that $me/ne < a$.

If $b \in S$ and $b < a$ then $a - b > z$; hence there exists a natural number $n$ such that $z < e/ne < a - b$. Now, by (38), there exists a natural number $m$ such that $nb \leqslant me$; we may take the smallest such $m$, hence $(m - 1)e < nb \leqslant me$, therefore

$$b \leqslant \frac{me}{ne} < b + \frac{e}{ne} < a.$$

(41) If $a, b \in S, a < b$, there exists integers $m, n$ such that $a < me/ne < b$.

For, if the inequality $me/ne < b$ implies $me/ne \leqslant a$ then, by property (40), we would have $b \leqslant a$, since $b$ is the least upper bound of all the elements $me/ne < b$ and $a$ is greater or equal than every such $me/ne$.

(42) We now consider the following correspondence from $S$ into the system of real numbers: to every element $me/ne \in S$ we associate the rational number $m/n$; to every element $a \in S$ we associate the real number $\alpha$, which is the least upper bound of all those rational numbers $m/n$ such that $me/ne < a$.

This correspondence is one-to-one: it follows easily from (41).

It is also onto the set of real numbers because any real number $\alpha$ is the least upper bound of all rational numbers $m/n < \alpha$; then $\alpha$ is the image, by this correspondence, of the element $a \in S$, equal to the least upper bound of all the corresponding elements $me/ne \in S$, where $m/n < \alpha$.

(43) Finally, it is easy to verify that the above mentioned correspondence preserves the operations and inequalities; that is, if $\alpha, \beta$ are real numbers corresponding respectively to the elements $a, b \in S$, then $\alpha + \beta$, $\alpha\beta$ correspond respectively to $a + b$, $ab$, and $\alpha < \beta$ if and only if $a < b$.

This concludes the proof that $S$ may be identified to the real numbers system, and provides an axiomatic presentation of the real numbers as the unique (up to isomorphism) complete ordered field.

Now, a brief comment on the economy of axioms.

It might well be that some of the axioms in the list may be logically deduced from the other ones. Then, we may delete these axioms and, instead, place them among the properties that may be proved logically; more appropriately, they should now be called propositions or theorems. However, the final fact is that the property in question is true for our mathematical system, whether it be assumed as an axiom, or appears as a consequence of other axioms.

# Appendix B

## Cardinal Number of Sets

As we mentioned on page 19, Cantor has proved that the set of rational numbers has infinitely fewer elements than the set of real numbers. How could this be, since both sets have infinitely many elements? Is it possible that a set is "more infinite" than another infinite set? If there are different ways for a set to be infinite, can we compare these ways?

These and other similar questions have been studied for the first time by Cantor in his epoch-making memoir *Contribution to the Founding of the Theory of Transfinite Numbers*. It has opened more than one branch in mathematics.

Here, we shall only consider one of these topics, which is more intimately connected with our aims.

We start with this straightforward question. What does it mean to count a set of objects?

It means that we label every object of the set by a natural number, one after the other, in their natural order, such as $x_1, x_2, x_3, \ldots$.

It may be that the set is exhausted when we have labeled its elements by, for example, the natural integers 1, 2, ..., 8. Then, we say that the set is finite and has 8 elements.

It may also be that, for every natural number $n$, there is in the set still another element, different from the already labeled elements $x_1, x_2, \ldots, x_n$. In this case, the set is said to be infinite.

In this naïve presentation of counting, what we really try to do is to establish some one-to-one correspondence (the labeling) between the given set and a part or the whole set of natural numbers, written in their natural order. As we shall see later, there are sets which cannot be counted by this process; that is, these sets will not be in one-to-one correspondence with any set of natural numbers.

The number of elements in a finite set must not depend on the special way the labeling is effected; in other words, two finite sets have the same number of elements if and only if there exists a one-to-one correspondence between these sets.

This promptly suggests a way of handling the counting of infinite sets. First, for infinite sets, there is no reason to label its elements by means of natural numbers; these are mostly appropriate for the counting of finite sets. For infinite sets, no "comparison set" (such as that of the natural numbers) appears in an obvious way. Therefore, instead of comparing each set with a standard set, we simply compare sets among themselves. The idea of equivalence classes, discussed in the text, plays an outstanding role.

We say that two sets, $A$ and $B$, are EQUIPOTENT, and we write $A \approx B$, when there exists a one-to-one and onto correspondence between the elements of $A$ and of $B$.

The following properties are clearly verified.

Reflexive property: $A \approx A$

Symmetric property: if $A \approx B$, then $B \approx A$

Transitive property: if $A \approx B$ and $B \approx C$, then $A \approx C$

If we are dealing with a certain collection of sets, we may, therefore, organize them into classes of equipotent sets: two sets are in the same class exactly when they are equipotent; otherwise they are in different classes.

Two distinct classes certainly have no set in common.

Thus, whatever the nature of their elements, sets belonging to the same class share the following property; the possibility of being put into one-to-one correspondence.

Each class of equipotent sets is called a CARDINAL NUMBER.

We shall denote the class of sets, in our collection, which are equipotent to a given set $A$ by $\#A$ (cardinal number of $A$). Therefore, for any two sets, $A$ is equipotent to $B$ if and only if $\#A = \#B$. We may also use other notations for cardinal numbers, for example signs like natural numbers when the set is finite. Thus we denote the cardinal number of the set $\{1, 2, \ldots, 8\}$ as 8. If, however, a set is not finite, our recourse is to invent new symbols to denote their cardinal numbers; they may be Greek letters or the traditional Hebrew letter $\aleph$ (aleph), with convenient subscripts.

The set of natural integers $\mathcal{N} = \{1, 2, \ldots, n, \ldots\}$, which is an infinite set, has cardinal number called "aleph zero," $\aleph_0$. It is said to be a COUNTABLE INFINITE SET. Every finite set is also considered as a countable set.

In summary, a set $A$ is said to be COUNTABLE when there exists a one-to-one correspondence from $A$ into the set of natural numbers.

One asks at once, "Aren't all sets countable?"

We try some examples of well-known sets to see whether they are countable. At the same time we shall record the properties discovered by examining these examples.

*The set of all integers* . . ., $-n$, . . ., $-2$, $-1$, $0$, $1$, $2$, . . ., $n$, . . . *is countable infinite*.

Indeed, we may establish the following one-to-one and onto correspondence between this set and $N$: to every even natural number $2n$ we associate $n - 1$, to every odd natural integer $2n - 1$ we associate $-n$; for example, $1 \rightarrow -1$, $2 \rightarrow 0$, $3 \rightarrow -2$, $4 \rightarrow 1$, $5 \rightarrow -3$, $6 \rightarrow 2$, and so on.

We notice at once that the above example illustrates that *an infinite set may have a proper part with the same cardinal number*. Conversely, *if a set is finite, it is not equipotent to any proper part of it*.

This assertion, no matter how obvious it may seem, needs proof. We must not forget how the notion of a finite set was defined; the set $A$ is finite when it is equipotent to *some* set $\{1, 2, . . ., n\}$; but it is not excluded in the definition that the same set $A$ be also equipotent to another set $\{1, 2, . . ., m\}$, with $m < n$. This is equivalent to saying that $\{1, 2, . . ., n\}$ is equipotent to the proper part $\{1, 2, . . ., m\}$. Of course, we may easily convince ourselves, by trial and error, when $n$ is not a large integer, that $\{1, 2, . . ., n\}$ cannot be equipotent to $\{1, 2, . . ., m\}$ unless $m = n$. But this is an experimentation and not a proof. The assertion can only be considered true if it has been proved and, therefore, we proceed to do so.

For this purpose, we assume that the assertion is false and we shall derive a contradiction. This means that there exists a natural number $n$ such that a set $A$, with $n$ elements, is equipotent to a proper part $B$. Among all natural numbers with the above property, we shall consider the smallest one, still denoted by $n$. Thus, a finite set $A'$ with less than $n$ elements cannot be equipotent to a proper part of it.

This integer $n$ cannot be 1 because any set $A$ with one element has only one proper part, that is, the empty set, and $A$ is not in one-to-one correspondence with the empty set.

Let $\phi : A \rightarrow B$ be a one-to-one correspondence from $A$ onto its proper part $B$; hence, there exists an element $a \in A$, $a \notin B$; we call $A'$ the set of all elements $a' \in A$, $a' \neq a$. Since $n > 1$, the set $A'$ is not empty, and it has, at most, $n - 1$ elements. The correspondence $\phi$ transforms $A'$ onto the set $B'$ of all elements of $B$, distinct from $\phi(a)$. The element $a$ is not in $B'$, since it is not in the set $B$; thus, $B'$ is a part of the set $A'$. But, as $A'$ has less than $n$ elements, $B'$ necessarily must be equal to $A'$. Since $B'$ is a proper part of $B$, the only possibility is that $B = A$, which is against our hypothesis.

Thus, the assertion must be true.

In certain presentations of the theory of cardinal numbers, this property is taken as the definition of a *finite set*.

Next we prove:

*The set of all rational numbers is countable infinite.*

By an argument similar to one already used, it is sufficient to prove that the set of all strictly positive rational numbers is countable infinite. It will be more convenient to prove that a certain set, containing that of strictly positive rational numbers, is infinite countable. Then, the set of rational numbers will be also countable, but it is not finite, since it contains all the integers; therefore, it will be countable infinite.

For the purpose of the proof, we arrange all the ordered pairs $(a, b)$ of natural numbers, with $b \neq 0$, and label one after the other by means of natural numbers, following the path indicated in Figure 15.

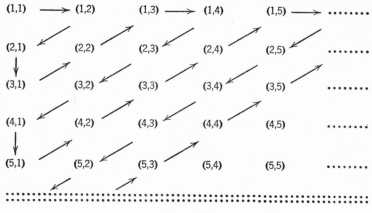

**Figure 15**

In this way, no ordered pair will be unaccounted for; it is an easy (but unnecessary) exercise to determine which will be the $n$th ordered pair in this labeling.

The set of all strictly positive rational numbers is in one-to-one correspondence with a proper subset of the above set of ordered pairs. As we have seen, every rational number $r > 0$ may be written, in unique way, in its irreducible form $r = a/b$ and we associate to $r$ the ordered pair $(a, b)$.

Let us comment about the preceding proof.

In the above arrangement of ordered pairs, each row is an infinite countable set. There are as many rows as natural numbers; that means, countably infinite many rows.

The whole set of ordered pairs is just the union of the sets that are its rows.

Therefore, by the same proof, we have also shown that:

*The union of countably many countable sets is a countable set.*

Now we give the first example of a set that is not countable.

*The set of all real numbers is not countable.*

We prove what at first glance might seem better: the set of all real numbers $x$ such that $0 \leqslant x < 1$ is not countable. But, indeed, this is not better, since the correspondence defined by

$$x \to \frac{2x(x-1)}{2x-1}$$

establishes a one-to-one mapping from the set of all $x$, $0 \leqslant x < 1$, onto the whole set of real numbers.

Every real number $x$, $0 \leqslant x < 1$, may be written in its decimal expansion as $0.a_1a_2a_3 \ldots a_n \ldots$ where each integer $a_i$ satisfies $0 \leqslant a_i \leqslant 9$; moreover, to make the decimal representation unique, it is not allowed that $a_i = 9$ for all indices $i$ larger than some index $i_0$.

If the set of all real numbers $x$, $0 \leqslant x < 1$, were countable, then we could label the decimal representations by natural numbers:

$$x_1 = 0.a_{11}a_{12}a_{13} \ldots a_{1n} \ldots$$
$$x_2 = 0.a_{21}a_{22}a_{23} \ldots a_{2n} \ldots$$
$$x_3 = 0.a_{31}a_{32}a_{33} \ldots a_{3n} \ldots$$
$$\ldots \ldots \ldots \ldots \ldots \ldots$$
$$x_n = 0.a_{n1}a_{n2}a_{n3} \ldots a_{nn} \ldots$$
$$\ldots \ldots \ldots \ldots \ldots \ldots$$

Now, we shall determine a real number $x$, $0 \leqslant x < 1$, given by its decimal representation and such that $x \neq x_n$ for every index $n$ — which shows that the above set cannot be countable.

We construct $x$ as follows: the $n$th digit in its decimal representation shall be any number $b_n$, $0 \leqslant b_n < 9$, $b_n \neq a_{nn}$, so that $x = 0.b_1b_2b_3 \ldots b_n \ldots$. Therefore, for every index $n$, we have $x \neq x_n$ since, at least, the $n$th digits are distinct.

Thus, we have proved that the set of real numbers is not countable. It contains the infinite countable set of rational numbers, and it is, therefore, reasonable to assert that it contains *infinitely many more elements* than the set of rational numbers since, as we have seen, any countable union of countable sets (such as that of rational numbers) would still be countable (and, therefore, still not as large as the set of real numbers).

# Bibliography

## Classical Works of Historical Importance

Cantor, Georg, *Contributions to the Founding of the Theory of Transfinite Numbers* (1895, 1897), Translated by P. Jourdain, Open Court, Chicago, 1915.
Cantor, Georg, *Gesammelte Abhandlungen*, Springer, Berlin, 1932.
Dedekind, Richard, *Stetigkeit und Irrationale Zahlen*, Vieweg, Braunschweig, 1872.
Peano, Giorgio, *Formulaire de Mathématiques*, Bocca, Turin, 1894–1908.

## Contemporary Books on Number Systems

Anderson, Kenneth W., and Hall, Dick W., *Sets, Sequences and Mappings*, Wiley, New York, 1963. *out of print*
Birkhoff, Garrett, and MacLane, Saunders, *A Survey of Modern Algebra*, MacMillan, New York, 1941.
Hamilton, Norman T., and Landin, Joseph, *Set Theory, the Structure of Arithmetic*, Allyn and Bacon, Boston, 1961.
Landau, Edmund, *Foundations of Analysis*, Translated by F. Steinhardt, Chelsea, New York, 1951.
Niven, Ivan, *Numbers: Rational and Irrational*, Random House, New York, 1961.
Olmsted, John M. H., *The Real Number System*, Appleton-Century-Crofts, New York, 1962.

## Other Books for Further Study

### Analysis

Apostol, Tom, *Mathematical Analysis*, Addison-Wesley, Reading, 1957.
Courant, Richard, *Differential and Integral Calculus*, translated by E. J. McShane, Blackie, London, 1934.
Eggleston, H. G., *Elementary Real Analysis*, The University Press, Cambridge, 1962.
Hardy, G. H., *A Course in Pure Mathematics*, The University Press, Cambridge, 1947.

*135*

### Set Theory and Foundations

Halmos, Paul R., *Naïve Set Theory*, Van Nostrand, Princeton, 1960.
Hausdorff, Felix, *Set Theory*, translated by J. R. Aumann, Chelsea, New York, 1957.
Kamke, Erich, *Theory of Sets*, translated by F. Bagemihl, Dover, New York, 1950.
Wilder, Raymond L., *Introduction to the Foundation of Mathematics*, Wiley, New York, 1952

### Topology

Kelley, John L., *General Topology*, Van Nostrand, New York, 1955.
Mendelsohn, Bert, *Introduction to Topology*, Allyn and Bacon, Boston, 1962.

of original order, 15% handling charge on all
turns will be accepted if polypack wrapping

s not returned to our warehouse with proper

r was in adoption quantity *(25 or more)*

rror.

# ROBERT E. KRIEGER pub

P. O. Box 542
Huntington, N. Y. 11743
(516) 271-5252

SOLD TO

N. SUMA
VANITY FAIR MILLS - PLT. #6
MONROEVILLE, AL.   36460

| INVOICE DATE | INVOICE NO. | YOUR ORDER REF. | TYPE | 1 | 2 | 3 |
|---|---|---|---|---|---|---|
| 5-23-77 | H 1315 | 5-13-77 | | | | 3 |

| QUANTITY | IDENTIFICATION | AUTHOR AND T |
|---|---|---|
| 1 | | RIBENBOIM:  FUNCTIONS, |

NO RETURNS ACCEPTED WITHO
SEE REVERSE SIDE FO
PACKI

# Name Index

| | | |
|---|---|---|
| Pythagoras | 6th Century B.C. | Greece |
| Euler, L. | 1707–1783 | Switzerland |
| Bolzano, B. | 1781–1848 | Austria |
| Cauchy, A. L. | 1789–1857 | France |
| Weierstrass, K. W. T. | 1815–1897 | Germany |
| Heine, E. | 1821–1881 | Germany |
| Dedekind, R. | 1831–1916 | Germany |
| Schwarz, H. A. | 1843–1921 | Germany |
| Cantor, G. | 1845–1918 | Germany |
| Peano, G. | 1858–1932 | Italy |
| Minkowski, H. | 1864–1909 | Germany |
| Borel, E. | 1871–1956 | France |
| Lebesgue, H. | 1875–1941 | France |

# Subject Index